SEMINAR STUDIES IN HISTORY

Editor: Patrick Richardson

THE SCIENTIFIC REVOLUTION
of the
SEVENTEENTH CENTURY

SEMINAR STUDIES IN HISTORY

Editor: Patrick Richardson

A full list of titles in this
series will be found on the
back cover of this book

SEMINAR STUDIES IN HISTORY

THE SCIENTIFIC REVOLUTION
of the
SEVENTEENTH CENTURY

Robin Briggs, M.A.

Fellow of All Souls College,
Oxford

HARPER & ROW, PUBLISHERS
NEW YORK, EVANSTON, SAN FRANCISCO,
LONDON

Library of Congress Catalog Card Number 77–151340

Printed in Malta by St Paul's Press Ltd for Harper & Row, Publishers, Inc.

Contents

Note on the System of References

A bold number in round brackets (**5**) in the text refers the reader to the corresponding entry in the Bibliography section at the end of the book.

A bold number in square brackets, preceded by 'doc.' [**docs 6, 8**] refers the reader to the corresponding items in the section of Documents, which follows the main text.

Acknowledgements

We are grateful to the following for permission to reproduce copyright material.

Doubleday & Co. Inc. for an extract from *Discoveries and Opinions of Galileo* by Stillman Drake, Copyright © 1957 by Stillman Drake; Harvard University Press for an extract from *A Source Book in Astronomy* edited by Shapley and Howarth; Harvard University Press and The Loeb Classical Library for an extract from Aristotle's *The Physics*, VIII, translated by P. H. Wickstead and F. M. Cornford; Thomas Nelson & Sons Ltd for an extract from *Descartes: Philosophical Writings*, translated and edited by E. Anscombe and P. T. Geach; Royal Astronomical Society for extract from *Occasional Notes of the Royal Astronomical Society*, Vol. II, No. 10, translated by J. F. Dobson and S. Brodetsky; The Regents of the University of California for extracts from *The Mathematical Principles of Natural Philosophy* Under Scholium[1] To Axiums or Laws of Motion, and Book III, Proposition XIII, Theorem XIII, Rule III; The Warburg Institute for an extract from *Demonic and Spiritual Magic* by Dr D. P. Walker from pages 33–32; The Wellcome Trust for an extract from *Dr. Thomas Sydenham 1624–1689* by K. Dewhurst.

We have been unable to trace the copyright holders of *Two New Sciences* translated by Crew and de Salvio, and would appreciate any information that would enable us to do so.

Foreword

The history of ideas is at once a fascinating and a difficult subject. Fascinating, since it can so often illuminate our own attitudes and problems by reference to the struggles of previous generations, and can also give a new dimension to past ages usually approached through political or economic history. Difficult, because ideas change their meaning and importance according to the context in which they appear, and vary in their significance for different thinkers and different periods. This complicates the historian's task greatly: should he stress continuity by following the ideas themselves, or risk a certain incoherence to show the variety of individual responses to them?

The history of science up to the end of the seventeenth century raises problems of this kind in an acute form, and no solution can be entirely satisfactory. The present book, which is primarily a study of the internal development of the physical sciences, alternates between short studies of important thinkers and more general sections seeking to relate them to wider themes in both science and society. I have tried to give an understandable account of this complex story which does not reduce it to a list of discoveries. In order to do this within the scope of a short book, much has to be omitted, and occasional simplification has been inevitable. In particular, the prominence accorded to a few major figures may seem excessive, a reversion to the outmoded 'great men' approach. It can only be said that these men did tower over their contemporaries, and that there is no sphere in which individuals count for more than in intellectual life.

Although this book is designed for students with no previous knowledge of the subject, it is possible that a few sections may prove difficult to follow at a first reading. Rather than stopping to puzzle them out, the reader would be well advised to continue and go back to them later, if necessary turning to a fuller treatment by another author. Details matter less than the general theme, and I have tried to subordinate them to it. At the same time the extracts from contemporary works in the text and in the documentary appendix are intended to prevent the book from becoming too general and too little in touch with its subject matter. It cannot, of course, pretend to be more than a summary treatment of an enormous topic, many aspects of which are still highly controversial. I have inevitably drawn heavily on the work and ideas of other historians, and hope to repay the debt by arousing a continuing interest among students which may lead them to pursue the subject further. The short bibliography is merely an introduction to the very considerable quantity of excellent work produced in recent years.

Part One

BACKGROUND

1 The Historical Background

SCIENCE IN THE ANCIENT WORLD

Cosmologies—systems of belief in general laws governing the universe—have existed since prehistoric times. If the discoveries of modern anthropologists are any guide, they must have been universal from a very early stage of man's development. Certainly all those modern peoples we choose to describe as 'primitive' possess their own cosmologies, which are often both complex and ingenious. They serve important social and psychological functions, underpinning the communal lives of tribes and peoples, directing the activities of individuals. It is difficult, for those brought up within the modern Western culture, to understand the rigidity and power of such structures of thought, since the intellectual revolution which began with the Greeks has emancipated our civilisation from their hold. The scientific revolution which came to a climax in the seventeenth century played a vital part in this development, and can only be properly understood in relation to it. The scientists who made this revolution did so in a highly conscious way; they spoke of the 'new philosophy' and contrasted 'ancients' and 'moderns'. They undertook their speculations and experiments with a constant awareness of their wider implications, and in this way brought about fundamental changes in man's view of himself and his universe. Perhaps only the Greeks have ever surpassed the intellectual achievements of the men we shall be studying, and there are instructive comparisons to be drawn between them. We must in any case give some consideration to Greek science and philosophy, since it was from this legacy that all later developments evolved.

The great empires of the Near East were notable for their technical advances, in the arts of ruling, and in what we should now call technology—civil engineering, medicine, metalworking. They also produced the vital discovery of writing, and developed towards a phonetic script; only a literate bureaucracy could administer political units of this size and complexity. But this technology was turned to the service of a closed, totalitarian society, and was jealously guarded as the preserve of a small ruling class. There is no sign that any of these early civilisations produced any kind of abstract philosophical thought. Their complex writing was employed to preserve useful factual material, not as an aid to thought. But the innovations which remain at least partly sterile in their place of origin are often successfully developed by their borrowers. When, around the seventh century B.C., the Greeks became literate, it was the prelude to the greatest cultural breakthrough in human history. Released from the constricting social circumstances within which it had developed, the phonetic alphabet became a potent revolutionary force.

In non-literate society the transmission of culture takes place in such a way that it is perpetually adjusted to absorb inconsistencies which arise. The use of writing for similar purposes favours the emergence of an awareness of such inconsistencies, and of rational criticism. It fosters a sense of change, and the notion that the cultural inheritance contains error as well as truth. These trends were very important in determining the direction of Greek thought. Writing used as an aid to thought also alters the nature of language: the relationship between the word and the object it describes becomes more general and more abstract, and more closely connected with the particularities of person, place and time. The idea of 'logic', an immutable and impersonal mode of discourse which appeared for the first time among the Greeks, was a reflection of their new alphabetical culture. They did not find their new philosophical problems comfortable, any more than we now do the implications of Einstein's theory of relativity. The past possessed a high value for the Greeks, and they had no desire to see the present detached from it, yet the mythology which satisfied Homer was clearly inadequate in the eyes of sixth-century philosophers. They therefore sought to provide new explanations of the universe, couched in logical terms, which would permit men to know the extreme and ultimate causes, and to explain the phenomenon of movement. Movement puzzled the Greeks greatly, and in all Greek philosophy there is a tension between being and becoming, between things in time and things eternal. A state of great intellectual tension was created by the awareness of these problems, and the Greeks never found an adequate answer to them.

Their attempts to do so, however, produced a body of thought whose astonishing originality and range served as an inspiration for later seekers after the same ends. The theories of the Ionians and Pythagoreans, giving explanations of the world in terms of, respectively, its component parts or matter, and its mathematical organisation, were developed by Plato and Aristotle into brilliant systems. Many of the writings of both philosophers were preserved, and their influence on Western thought has been immeasurable. It is impossible to summarise such elaborate and sophisticated philosophical structures in the present context, but there was a clear contrast between their attitudes to the nature of the world, the subject matter of science. Plato was the heir of the Pythagoreans, and treated the sensible world as a dim and imperfect reproduction of an ideal world accessible only to the soul, and in which the Divine Ideas were visible in their true perfection and reality. Thus there was a coherent pattern underlying the apparent chaos of the world, but the misleading nature of imperfect appearances concealed it from man. Aristotle was Plato's pupil, but he had little time for these heady metaphysical schemes, and concentrated on the classification of the objects of sense. His world was a teleologically ordered structure, in which formal principles, 'Forms', were working in matter—the possibility of becoming—towards their own several perfections. The whole principle of nature was a passage from potential to actual in accordance with an inner tendency towards perfection, the nature of every created thing being to realise its own formal principle, its own particular end or excellence.

Aristotle's cosmology represents a great intellectual achievement, and any summary will inevitably fail to do him justice, even before one begins to point out his weaknesses. One of his guiding principles was that sense data must be trusted, and he therefore placed the earth, a solid immobile sphere, at the centre of the universe. This universe was finite, bounded by the sphere of the fixed stars, and the movements of the heavens above the sphere of the moon were explained by a system which was thought to possess both mathematical and physical reality. These regions were filled by the aether, the celestial element, which Aristotle visualised as a crystalline solid. The great diurnal sweep of the sphere of the fixed stars provided the primary motion of the heavens, while the vagrant motions of the planets (the Greek word means 'wanderer') were explained by a complex mechanism of transparent concentric spheres. Altogether there were fifty-five of these spheres, nestling together and working to and fro within one another. Seven of them carried those five of our planets known to the ancients, and the sun and moon, which were treated as planets for astronomical purposes. The other spheres were necessary to provide the mechanical means whereby the separate motions of the planets could maintain their relative independence of the primary motion of the outer sphere.

The mechanics of the system were more striking than its mathematical accuracy, and the astronomers of late antiquity were obliged to modify the latter to the point where they could no longer believe in the interlocking spheres as Aristotle had described them. The problems created by this breakdown between the two parts of the system, and the continued deficiencies of mathematical astronomy even after Ptolemy, were eventually to provide the springboard for the Copernican Revolution.

Like every other major scientific thinker from the fourth century onwards, Aristotle recognised that the earth was a sphere; belief in a flat earth was almost as unreasonable on the evidence available in late antiquity as it is today. But the sphere of the earth was part of the larger area of the sublunar world, which contained the four elements, a classification of matter he had borrowed from the Ionians. It has never been absolutely clear whether Aristotle thought of the elements as actual substances or as the forms which resided in them, but this is not an essential point for the understanding of his system. In descending order of weight (and nobility) the elements were fire, air, water and earth. Each was possessed of two of the four basic qualities, of which the first-named was primary; thus fire was hot and dry, air moist and hot, water moist and cold, and earth dry and cold. By a change in one of its qualities one element could change into another, as the ashes of a fire become earth.

If the elements had been able to follow their natural propensities unhindered, they would have formed themselves into a series of perfect spheres mirroring those of the heavens, with fire the nearest below the moon, then air, water, and finally earth. But the movement of the heavenly spheres, acting through the sphere of the moon, was seen by Aristotle as creating a constant disturbance among the elements, which were therefore never to be found in their pure state. Various mixtures of the elements were made to represent every kind of matter known to man, and the behaviour of the physical world explained by the constant attempts of the elements to return to their proper stations in the sublunary sphere. It requires a conscious effort of the imagination to realise how brilliantly this cosmology applied common sense notions to the scientific problems of the day, and how difficult it was to oppose it in the light of everyday sensory experience. An enormous amount of data seemed to support it, from the influence of the moon on the tides to the falling of heavy bodies.

This last example draws attention to the further ramifications of the system, and in particular to Aristotle's mechanics. These too were based on common sense reasoning, with the first axiom being that every motion presupposes a mover, which must either be present in the thing moved or in contact with it throughout the motion. There were complex philosophical problems arising from this doctrine, but in practice the motion of heavy bodies falling to earth was regarded as the natural action produced by the inherent desire of the elements to take up their proper place in the world—in the case of earth the centre. Like all natural motion in the sublunary sphere, their fall was rectilinear, as opposed to the perfect, eternal and circular motion of the spheres. Problems really began, however, with the motion of projectiles, and we shall see how important this topic was to be for later scientists [**doc. 1**]. Another Aristotelian position which was to be the source of later controversy was the denial of the possibility of a void; the universe was full, and its perfect interaction could only be maintained in this way if action at a distance were to be admitted.

The doctrine of the elements which Aristotle took from his predecessors was paralleled by other fourfold divisions employed by Greek thinkers, notably the medical theory of the humours. These fitted neatly into the general scheme, and were to be the basis for the medical writings of the Alexandrian physician Galen, through whom they passed to medieval doctors. The humours were: blood, which was warm and moist, and associated with the spring; yellow bile, warm and dry, summer; black bile, cold and dry, autumn; and phlegm, cold and moist, winter. The four seasons were in their turn associated with the four ages of man, and with the four temperaments, the sanguine, the choleric, the melancholy, and the phlegmatic. In this way man became the microcosm, the little world which reflected the macrocosm or big world of the universe.

Plato's immediate influence was particularly strong in mathematics and geometry, and Euclid, whose *Elements* were the summary of the Greek achievement in this field, was a student in Plato's Academy. Mathematics did not, however, make the progress that might have been expected from this point onwards: the failure to

7

develop the arithmetical methods of the Babylonians was crucial in this area. In any case, the predominant influence in the physical and biological sciences was that of Aristotle, and his ingenious and plausible theories had little use for the more advanced forms of mathematics. Although alternative systems were proposed by later philosophers, notably the Stoics, these did not differ much in general style and shared the bias against the mathematical approach to nature. It had been a weakness of Greek science from the start that its practitioners were anxious to run before they could walk, and to propound general theories based on very scanty empirical evidence. Aristotle had now created a physical world picture which seemed to accommodate the observed phenomena, and no serious alternative emerged to challenge it for two millennia.

Many important and valuable discoveries were made during the Hellenistic period, but they did not lead to a revaluation of the accepted cosmology. In the absence of a clearly defined experimental method, and especially in view of the qualitative rather than quantitative nature of Aristotelian physics, there was little chance of this occurring. The Greeks had developed the logical and mathematical tools necessary for the examination and explanation of nature, but their application of them had only been partially successful (**14**, **15**, **16**, **17**).

This account has concentrated on physics, since this was to prove the critical area in the medieval and early modern development of science. In medicine, chemistry and biology most of the general theories held by the Greeks were both erroneous and ultimately fruitless, although a good deal of empirical data was accumulated. In these fields they can be said to have aroused the intellectual interest of later thinkers, but not to have defined the problems or suggested the answers to them. The division of knowledge into separate categories was one of the most important general contributions of the Greeks, and because almost all medieval science was in effect a commentary on their legacy, these divisions were continued into the modern period. This was to prove a mixed blessing; while such a framework was essential, it often inhibited cross-fertilisation and free thinking.

THE TRANSMISSION OF THE GREEK HERITAGE

The intellectual triumphs of the Greeks reflected not only the effects of literacy and the genius of individuals, but also the remarkable political and social advances of the sixth and fifth centuries B.C. The free, individualistic, rational environment of this period had important psychological consequences: the emergence of man as the central figure in the picture of the universe, and the gradual increase in the value of the individual's personality in the world of man. The disastrous Peloponnesian War marked the end of Greek democracy, and by the end of the third century there was an enormous gap between the rational philosophers and the general populace. The intellectuals had no understanding of the passions, which they wished to banish as mere errors of judgment, and the strain of living up to their intellectual freedom became overpowering. In the second century the ancient superstitions of the East became rife, and astrological determinism replaced rationalism. The collapse of Greek thought was far from complete, and in Alexandria and other centres important work continued into the period of the late Roman Empire. But the almost excessive confidence which had generated the great cosmological theories was lost, and even men like the great astronomer Ptolemy (in the second century A.D.) were filling the gaps in a basically Aristotelian world picture, although they might reject some of its details. As for the Romans, they produced no scientists of any note at all, despite their civil engineering achievements. The most probable explanation for this surprising failure lies in the pragmatic, non-abstract nature of both Roman culture and the classical Latin language—which may also account for the lack of important Roman philosophers.

The coming of Christianity effected yet further changes. The early Fathers were generally hostile to pagan science, and stressed the supreme importance of divine revelation. But the view also arose that there was a place for both reason and revelation, and that they could be complementary. The most influential of all the Latin Fathers, St. Augustine, although he placed the authority of the scriptures and divine revelation above all science, recognised that God manifested himself in the world, and that study of the world could therefore help to reveal divine wisdom.

Augustine was deeply influenced by the Neoplatonism of Plotinus,

9

a mystical development of Plato's philosophy which placed relatively little value on science, and was a dominant influence on early Christianity. Aristotle was regarded with deep scepticism, in so far as his works were known, and his later predominance in Christian thought would have been quite inconceivable at this date. The attitude of Christians became of great importance with the collapse of the Roman Empire and the onset of the Dark Ages. The scientific and philosophical tradition of Greece was now preserved by three different agencies: the Eastern Empire, the Arabs, and the Christian Church. All, in their different ways, distorted the tradition according to their own predispositions and preoccupations, and only with the reuniting of the severed parts in the medieval and Renaissance periods did the advance of science begin again on a broad front.

In the Byzantine Empire science played a small part. The manuscripts of the works of the Greek philosophers were preserved and copied, but for their religious rather than their scientific content. The ritualised, formal world of Constantinople was interested in Plato's mysticism rather than his mathematics, and had little time for Aristotle at all. The Arabs, on the other hand, considered Aristotle the greatest of philosophers, and were the primary means by which his works were transmitted to Western Europe. Arabic science was largely derivative from that of the Greeks, with an admixture of rather fanciful material on astrology, alchemy, and similar subjects. But in mathematics the Arabs did make significant advances, introducing really effective forms of algebra and trigonometry, and improving on earlier geometry. They also developed a numerical notation which we still employ, ultimately derived from India, in which the value of a figure is determined by its place. There was never any real sign that the Arabs were possessed of sufficient originality or critical spirit to attempt a basic reappraisal of the whole corpus of scientific knowledge, but their achievements were very considerable, and without them later events in Western Europe might never have taken place. Their work on optics raised problems which stimulated some of the best work of scholastic philosophers, and their alchemical experiments and astrological tables were to have value for later chemists and astronomers.

THE SCIENCE OF THE MIDDLE AGES

By the ninth century there were signs that a revival of cultural activity was taking place in Western Europe, and that the Church, the guardian of the educational tradition inherited from the Roman Empire, was broadening her intellectual horizons. Gradually the derivative compilations of such late Latin authors as Boethius and Isidore of Seville were supplemented by translations from the Arabic, and the majority of the works of Aristotle became known in the West in the course of the twelfth century. Historians have long been accustomed to speak of the twelfth-century renaissance, in order to characterise a period of intellectual history dominated by the rediscovery of Greek philosophy and science. Although Aristotle was the greatest single influence, his works were transmitted in a very imperfect form, and with a considerable admixture of Platonic metaphysics. From the summary of his system given earlier it should be easy to see how the division between the corrupt sublunary world and the perfect motions of the celestial spheres could be assimilated to the doctrine of the Fall of Man, and both these in their turn to the Platonic notions of the world as an imperfect representation of the divine order.

This first renaissance was largely the product of the monastic schools, and notably that of Cluny in France. But the thirteenth century saw the development of certain of these schools into universities, among which Paris, Oxford and Padua became the most important. The growth of institutions where learned men could live and work together, and instruct students, was clearly of the greatest importance for Western civilisation. But it also had a less welcome side, for most students of this period were very young men, in their middle teens, and this favoured methods of teaching which did not encourage intellectual independence or originality. The universities were to play a relatively small direct part in the scientific revolution, although the stimulus their establishment gave to general culture was enormous.

The thirteenth century was also notable for the consolidation, among the clerics who taught in the new universities, of a body of doctrine about the nature of the world, known as scholasticism. This was a combination of well-defined logical method with a basically Aristotelian cosmology, and reached its peak with the theological

11

and philosophical works of St. Thomas Aquinas. This Dominican friar separated faith and reason, and then reconciled them. For Aquinas accepted the Aristotelian principle that sensory experience was the basis of all human knowledge, and then directed this knowledge towards proving the truth of revelation.

Thomism never acquired the status of an official doctrine in the Middle Ages: instead it added vigour to controversies that were already in existence. Oddly enough the majority of original contributions to science during the thirteenth century came from men with more transcendental, metaphysical beliefs, such as the Englishmen Robert Grosseteste and Roger Bacon. The philosophical basis of the thirteenth century systems was soon subjected to a withering attack by William of Ockham, who denied the possibility of a valid association between faith and reason. He claimed that it was impossible to draw valid generalisations about a group or·class of things from the individuals which composed it; in any case sense experience was unreliable, for God might deceive man. Theology was an affair of faith, and had nothing to do with the form of the natural world. Like Thomism, Ockhamism never became a generally accepted doctrine. But it effectively destroyed any hope the former had of becoming so, and left the relationship between theology and natural science in a very fluid and uncertain condition.

The significance of these theological and philosophical arguments for science was very considerable. Such scientific research as was undertaken during the Middle Ages was very largely the work of clerics, who had undergone a thorough training in this kind of debate, and were well aware of the implications of their activities. It is quite possible that the establishment of a Thomist synthesis would have had a cramping and deadening effect on scientific speculation, whereas the absolute duality proposed by Ockham left far more room for manoeuvre. At a more popular level the Aristotelian cosmology was certainly associated with God's ordering of the world, but the handful of outstanding intellectuals who were adventuring on the frontiers of knowledge had no need to take this line. The failure of the Church to accept pagan science unreservedly was in the long run to prove to her own discomfiture and the advantage of science. The way was being prepared for a view of nature as a separate entity, governed by its own laws independently of God, and the triumph of this attitude was to leave faith exposed to the assaults of reason.

In tracing the relationship between theology and science little has been said about medieval science itself. Although by modern standards the amount of scientific work done may not have been very great, there is still an enormous mass of surviving material to demonstrate its extent. Little of it, however, would strike a modern observer as 'scientific' in its subject matter or approach. Catalogues of wonders, strange creatures and monsters combine with incomprehensible alchemical tracts and elaborate astrological treatises to give an impression of luxuriant decadence. Much of the medical literature seems similarly removed from the spirit of rational enquiry. Only the difficult and involved writings of those thinkers who tackled the mathematical and geometrical problems associated with optics, kinematics and dynamics stand out by their more severe approach to scientific proof.

In particular, the question of the motion of projectiles and its nature produced important work by men like Jean Buridan in Paris and Thomas Bradwardine in Oxford. These men and the other fourteenth-century thinkers who occupied themselves with kinematics did not achieve any major breakthrough, and remained largely the prisoners of an Aristotelian conceptual system: like their fellow scholastics, they saw their task as filling in gaps and removing inconsistencies in a generally accepted world picture. But they were responsible for the creation of a tradition which encouraged the investigation through mathematics of a number of crucial problems connected with the movement of bodies through time and space. The Parisian Nicole Oresme even used figures resembling graphs in his work on dynamics, although the immediate influence of this step was negligible. By handing down to their successors, not merely an identifiable set of vital questions, but also some of the mathematical techniques necessary for their solution, the scholastic physicists paved the way for Galileo (**18, 19, 20**).

Far more attention was paid to astronomy, and again advanced opinions were in the air: both Oresme and Buridan discussed the possibility that the daily motion of the heavens could be explained by the rotation of the earth. But in the face of scriptural assertions of the immobility of the earth, no one was prepared to put the idea forward as anything but an interesting hypothesis. The chief business of astronomers was in any case not to explain how the heavens worked, but to provide accurate tables of planetary movements for the use of professional astrologers. Frequent ecclesiastical condemnations did nothing to destroy the general belief in the efficacy of astrology,

13

since the Church did not deny this, but merely pronounced it unlawful and sinful.

The relatively sophisticated calculations involved in these predictions were based on the astronomical system of Ptolemy, with its complicated maze of circles filling the heavens in an attempt to reduce the motions of planets to combinations of the only movement permitted above the moon, that in a circle. The trouble with this system, apart from the fact that it gave extremely unreliable and inaccurate predictions, was that it could not be reconciled with the Aristotelian physical view of the heavens. Since Ptolemy's circles crossed one another repeatedly, it was impossible for them to be solid bodies. As a mid-seventeenth-century critic, John Webster, was to remark scornfully:

> And if there were any motion at all it must needs be with confrication, and attrition, and so without plenty of some oily substance, would not cause Pythagoras his spherical musick, but an unheard-of rumbling noise, such surely as possessed the brains of those that were the first Authors of this mad and extravagant opinion.

But three centuries before no such iconoclastic attitude was even conceivable; the inconsistency was accepted, and no serious effort made to reconcile the mathematical and physical pictures of the universe (**19, 20**).

The appreciation of problems in physics and astronomy by fourteenth-century scientists marked an important advance towards the revival of serious discussion about the nature of the world. But the fruits of their work were slow to appear, and for much of the fifteenth century scientific activity appeared to be on the decline rather than the increase. To understand why this should have been the case, it is necessary to see how the science of this period was associated with a general world outlook, and with the state of society itself.

It has already been emphasised that the Aristotelian scheme of the world had a very great common sense appeal, and seemed to be confirmed on every side by the most casual glance at the evidence. To the men of the Middle Ages the universe was organised according to a divine pattern, into which men were granted a limited though real understanding. The earth they inhabited was the centre of the universe, because composed of the heaviest and grossest matter, and was subject to the perpetual disruptive effects of the continual war of the elements in the sublunary sphere. It was only through the abundant grace of God that some precarious order was maintained for the benefit of sinful man, and it was the latter's duty to play his part by supporting the divinely given hierarchies in his society. Popes, bishops and kings were the spiritual and temporal representatives of divine authority, and even their political opponents paid lip-service to their rights in this capacity. Order in the heavens, in the state, in the family, among animals and plants, all were linked by the Great Chain of Being which brought God, through his angels, into contact with man and all the lower orders of life on earth (54, 55).

It was not surprising that the scientists were unable to extricate themselves from the powerful grasp of this unified cosmology and break with the dogmas of Aristotle. Indeed, they can be seen as the products of a confident and expanding era, sustained by these very beliefs, and in which the Crusades, the strengthening of monarchical authority, increasing trade, and rising population were all evidence of vitality. Similarly, the decline in their activity during the late fourteenth and fifteenth centuries was associated with the disasters which overtook medieval civilisation as a whole during this period. The greatest of these was the Black Death of 1348–9, which probably reduced the population of Europe by at least a third. Whatever the reasons for the arrival of this plague, its effects were certainly rendered more grave by the condition of the populations it attacked. There were too many people trying to live off a relatively small productive capacity, and in consequence they were underfed and very vulnerable to contagious disease.

The Middle Ages had failed to find an answer to the problem of food supplies: agricultural and industrial techniques had simply not advanced fast enough to meet the new demands on them. This failure of medieval technology was not directly connected with medieval science: the latter was largely a breach of theology and philosophy, trying to deepen the understanding of God's world. For most laymen its only practical application was probably through astrology and magical practices. But we can hardly doubt that there is a close link between science and technology, and that the limited ambitions of most medieval scientists indicated a lack of belief in man's ability to bring about effective changes in the natural environment. This pessimism was intensified as medieval civilisation showed increasing signs of breakdown and loss of confidence. Life had always been lived under the fear of the Day of Judgment, but after the arrival of the plague—which returned repeatedly—this fear became a conviction that the world was entering on its last age. Growing political anarchy, important economic changes, and the threatening advance of the Turks all seemed to confirm that the collapse of the established order was imminent.

THE RENAISSANCE

All was not dark, however, and this era of despair also saw the emergence of new intellectual and social trends which were to fill the void left by the progressive disintegration of the medieval world view. The most notable of these new forces was that complex and fertile intellectual movement we call the Renaissance. Its causes, and its very nature, have always been the subject of arguments among historians, and we cannot concern ourselves seriously with them here. But its consequences were to be of the greatest importance for the scientific revolution, even if their influence cannot be precisely measured.

Oddly enough it was in Italy, the traditional centre of Christendom, that the movement began. The disruption of political order in the peninsula had been rapid, and was accompanied by the appearance of independent city states in the north, possessed of important trading networks. At the same time it was to Italy that the scholars and manuscripts of the Byzantine empire came during the fourteenth and fifteenth centuries as the Turks advanced through the eastern Mediterranean. Not only the works of Plato, but those of many other Greek and Alexandrian philosophers, became available once more for the study of the new humanist scholars of Florence, Padua, Venice and other cities. Paradoxically enough, these men still thought they were engaged in restoring lost knowledge from the past, when in fact they misunderstood much of what they rediscovered, and employed it to ends of whose novelty they were scarcely themselves aware. What had begun as a mainly literary movement centred in a few North Italian towns quickly became a revolutionary current of ideas, which spread not only across all Europe, but into every form of intellectual activity.

By the beginning of the sixteenth century there were many signs that the long period of exhaustion which had followed the collapse of the medieval political and social systems was being replaced by a new era of expansion and energy. Already Columbus had discovered the New World, a fitting prelude to the new age. The monarchs of Europe were reasserting their authority over their subjects, while the centralised nation-state began to emerge as the basic unit of politics. The population was increasing rapidly, and labour became sufficiently abundant to encourage the cultivation of marginal land and the stepping-up of industrial activity. As the demand for more food, aided by the influx of precious metals from America, produced a massive inflation, greater social mobility was encouraged; even the rich had to grow richer if they were not to go under. It was an exciting world, but a dangerous one, and the realistic political thought of Machiavelli caught its spirit so well that it both attracted and appalled his contemporaries. For if on the one hand there was a new dynamism and self-confidence, on the other there was fear and insecurity, and a constant sense of danger. The intensity with which Renaissance men experienced life is revealed in the art and literature they produced, in which we can see both a terrible awareness of the transitory nature of existence and a fierce determination to assert their individuality against it.

A similar heightening of experience was apparent in the other great intellectual upheaval of the sixteenth century, the Reformation. In many ways, as with the Renaissance, its roots lay in a desire to reestablish the original and purer state of things which was thought to have been overlaid with irrelevant medieval additions. But again the results were far more revolutionary than the intentions. Not only did the new doctrines inspire their adherents to defy the established powers of the world in the name of their beliefs; they also aroused a corresponding reaction in the Catholic Church. The Counter-Reformation was far from being a purely reactionary movement, and often associated itself with popular religious sentiments. Both Henry III and Henry IV of France were to be assassinated by Catholic fanatics, who thought the principles of hierarchy less important than the interests of the true faith. The breakdown of the traditional association between religion and the social order not merely added to the general sense of insecurity, it also made it easier for men to think in a secular manner, treating religion as a separate issue. In this way too the medieval strait-jacket burst open during the sixteenth century.

The rapid spread of the Reformation was largely due to one of the inventions which have done most to influence the history of mankind. The introduction of printing from movable type had made it possible for knowledge and ideas to be disseminated with a new speed and accuracy, and was rapidly to encourage the development of both propaganda and public controversy on a large scale. The printing of the Bible both in cheap editions and vernacular translations was in itself an act of subversion against established authority of the greatest significance, for it enabled every literate person to form private opinions on the central moral and religious texts of his culture.

But printing was only one of the technological developments which were to contribute to the shaping of the new age. While gunnery was still at a relatively early stage, it had already brought about major changes in the art of war, and it perhaps gave some encouragement to the study of ballistics. It was also associated with progress in metalworking and the manufacture of explosives. These last were further employed in mining, which not only produced ores for the metalworkers, but encouraged some primitive investigations of geology. The discovery of America and the opening up of trade with the East emphasised the advances made in shipbuilding and navigation, and had important consequences. New plants and animals, new peoples, and new ideas were found in lands of whose existence the ancients had been ignorant, to give the sensation of an expanding world. The improvement in glass-making technique provided flasks and containers for the alchemists, and was also to lead in the seventeenth century to the telescope and microscope. All these practical discoveries, and many others there is no space to mention here, were to be exploited by the scientists in support of their investigations (**21, 23**).

It should not be thought that the influence of the Renaissance on scientific enquiry was a simple or straighforward one. There is much to be said for the view that sixteenth-century 'natural philosphers' were less sophisticated or genuinely scientific in their attitudes than their medieval predecessors. This had a good deal to do with the nature of the writings from antiquity which had been rediscovered. They were very largely philosophical, and showed a considerable bias in favour of a mystical approach to knowledge. Not only the works of Plato himself, but also an enormous quantity of both Neoplatonic and Gnostic theorising came into vogue, and brought with it a considerable dose of irrationalism. For a long time more importance was attached to texts of the latter kind, dating from the early centuries of the Christian era, than to those of the great period of Greek thought. This preference was an example of the dangers of an excessive emphasis on the past. Since Renaissance thinkers believed they were bringing back to light divinely given knowledge which had been lost at some stage in the past history of man, they were unduly credulous when dealing with texts they thought to be examples of this lost wisdom.

For a long time their intellectual independence was very limited, and they frequently fooled themselves into seeing great profundities in what was little more than obscure nonsense. In truth they had no conception at all of the formidable difficulties of scientific enquiry, and thought in terms of revolutionary discoveries which would reveal the key to the whole structure of the universe at one stroke. This was perhaps a useful blindness, since had they realised how far there was to go, they might have given up in despair. But it was also responsible for a great deal of careless and speculative activity which arrived nowhere, and the obsession with short cuts to knowledge produced many wildly improbable claims and projects. The rediscovery of the scientific texts of the Hellenistic period, with their high mathematical achievement, such as the writings of Archimedes and Apollonios, was vital in the long run but strangely uninfluential at first.

The comprehensive nature of Aristotelian science had a bad influence on many sixteenth-century thinkers: they naturally wanted to find a replacement system which would possess the same scope. The most restrained of the general theories put forward was probably that of Telesio, who proposed heat and cold as the basic qualities of the celestial and terrestial worlds respectively. All natural phenomena were explained by the contraction and condensation caused by cold and the expansion and rarefaction from heat. All this change had effected was the substitution of two qualities for Aristotle's four; the style of thought had not altered. If nature was conceived in terms of an undefined basic substance worked on by 'form', whether Aristotelian or not, almost everything could be explained away by a certain amount of logical juggling.

It was through exasperation with the endless complications of this sort of philosophising that so many Renaissance intellectuals proclaimed themselves anti-Scholastic, although they could not produce satisfactory alternatives of their own. For a large number of them the way out seemed to lie through magic, and in the age of the great European witch-hunts this was a tempting if dangerous prospect. The reason for these witch-hunts was almost certainly the obsession of the upper classes at this period with the occult. When judges and magistrates took popular beliefs seriously, major panics could easily result.

There was no real dividing line between witchcraft and black magic, as the Faust legend shows: the things of this world being under the power of the devil, he had the ability to bestow them on those who would serve him in exchange. It was widely believed that the magic arts had been known to the sages of antiquity, such as Zoroaster and Hermes Trismegistus, and that their secrets were concealed in the mystical texts newly recovered from the East. Like so many other errors, this belief in magic had its positive side. Under the influence of Pythagorean and Neoplatonic thought, a good many people sought the key to the organisation of the universe in mathematical terms, although they usually did so in an uncritical and profitless way. However, as we shall see, some of the greatest figures of the scientific revolution were not merely interested in these ideas, but were deeply involved with practical activities we can only call magical [**doc. 2**] (**23, 27, 28, 60, 61, 62**).

The Renaissance artists were also interested in mathematics, and helped to change man's view of his world. Instead of producing beautiful symbolic artefacts to support the great myths of the Christian Church, they wanted to concentrate on man and his universe, and to depict nature realistically. In order to achieve this they were obliged to employ Euclidean geometry in tackling the problems of perspective, and in doing so gave expression to the idea that the universe was constructed according to a geometrical model. Leonardo de Vinci, Piero della Francesca, Albrecht Durer, and Michelangelo were all far more than mere painters; they were deeply interested by discoveries in mathematics, and held very positive views about the general structure of the universe. Through their art and writings they encouraged the development of man's visual perceptions. We should remember that in the sixteenth century touch, smell, and hearing were relatively more important senses than they are now compared to vision, and much more of people's everyday information about the world was gathered through them. These are more flexible senses than vision, and more closely connected with the emotions; their preponderance was a vital factor in the preservation of the medieval world picture, since they tended to repress awareness of inconsistencies.

The increased importance of visual perception can be associated with quantitative science. The measurement of dimensions and motion, for example, are essentially visual operations. But it was also part of that gradual emancipation of the individual from communal pressures which is perhaps the great underlying theme of the Renaissance. The relationship between man and his environment was becoming more intellectualised and less instinctual, and his mind and personality were increasingly free to follow the Greek aphorism most favoured in the Renaissance: 'Know thyself.' The search was to become a search for a new system of the world.

2 The Sixteenth-century Forerunners

Although the sixteenth century did not see the emergence of any system which could pretend to compete with that of Aristotle, a handful of outstanding figures emerged during its course. They made powerful and effective attacks on certain aspects of the established world view, and it was through their pioneering efforts that the way was prepared for such successors as Descartes and Newton. An examination of their work will enable us to identify the main trends in scientific thought during this period.

PARACELSUS, 1493–1541

No single individual could represent the contradictions and inconsistencies of the Renaissance spirit better than this Swiss-German physician, who burned the *Canon* of Avicenna (a standard medical textbook) in public, and was called the 'Luther of medicine'. It was evident enough that reform was urgently needed in the medical sciences; some simple surgical operations apart, the sick had little to hope for from professional attention, and much to fear. Medieval doctors performed their diagnosis according to the theory of the humours, and thought they need only restore their imaginary balance within the body for a cure to be effected. Even had the principles been sound, the remedies prescribed were pathetically limited: bleeding, purging, and the use of 'medicines' apparently chosen for their special nastiness.

To this tradition Parcelsus opposed a typically magical conception of the universe, with alchemy as the key to understanding. Aristotle, he said, was a useless guide, since his logic could only explain its own statements, not lead to new discoveries; instead of this sterile approach, divine revelation was needed. The adept should seek this knowledge through mystical experience and experiment in nature. In fact the four elements remained a basic feature of Paracelsian doctrine, but they were joined, in an extremely vague relationship, by three principles: sulphur, mercury, and salt. These were associated with the combustible, vaporous, and solid constituents of matter respectively, and a simple operation such as distillation could be held to demonstrate their presence beyond any reasonable doubt.

Developing the theories of the alchemists, Paracelsus considered the Creation to have been a divine chemical separation, when the elements and principles had been imposed by God on the basic material of the universe. He drew on the common stock of Neoplatonic and Hermetic notions to illustrate and support his theories, and his medical teaching was based on the macrocosm–microcosm analogy by which man was the epitome of the universe. As the world was a kind of vast chemical laboratory, in which natural phenomena represented the interactions of the elements and principles, so the body of man was also open to the influence of chemical reactions. Paracelsus did reject the four humours, and thought of diseases as external or internal forces affecting particular organs of the body. They could therefore be combated by the use of natural materials which would act as chemical antidotes, and this belief led to the use of medicines derived from metals. This had already been done by earlier physicians, but so strongly did the practice become associated with Paracelsus that from soon after his death anyone who followed it could expect to be described as a Paracelsian.

A mass of legends quickly grew up around the life of Paracelsus, and innumerable miraculous cures were attributed to him, although as one of his early critics, Erastus, pointed out, there was little reason to think him more successful than other doctors of the period. While the Paracelsian attitude to diagnosis was certainly superior to that of the Galenists, and the attempt to impose a strict control on the quantities of drugs applied was a genuine advance, there were still such areas of ignorance about the functioning of the body and the nature of disease that the practical gains were small. The use of mercury preparations for the treatment of the new scourge of syphilis certainly cured some sufferers—but overdosing by ignorant charlatans probably killed more.

If the medieval physicians had preceded Paracelsus in the use of chemical medicines, they had only done so on a small scale. But under the influence of his great reputation a rapidly growing number of doctors experimented with new drugs, and found patients

B

eager to try the effects. Even relatively conservative men who rejected the mystical and religious side of Paracelsus's teachings did not necessarily deny his importance or refuse to follow his methods. The name 'iatrochemist', given to the physicians who used chemical medicines, often indicated merely a position of this kind, not outright Paracelsianism. There were so many bitter struggles between Galenists and Paracelsians in the medical faculties and guilds of Europe over the century after his death that it is too easy to think of opposing parties, when in reality the dividing lines were very confused. If the immediate results were not spectacular, the emphasis on chemical remedies was still of great importance for the future. It encouraged experiment and observation, and also gave a considerable stimulus to chemistry itself.

This strange combination of mysticism, alchemy, and opposition to the accepted truths of medical practice therefore helped to encourage new approaches in several directions. It provided a powerful alternative to the Galenic tradition, which aided those who were dissatisfied with the existing state of their science to strike out into new paths. As Paracelsus himself always insisted, it was new truth against old error, and this was justified at least in his general conception of disease as a specific complaint calling for a particular treatment. Even the notion of the universe as a great chemical experiment was not entirely ridiculous, as we who live in the age of nuclear physics must admit. Among the new medicines and the chemical experiments inspired by the theory there were some of genuine value, however illusory the ideas on which they were based. And even if their scientific results had been less impressive still, the writings of Paracelsus added to the weight of the general assault on the teachings of antiquity, and emphasised to contemporaries as they do to us that this was an era of conflict between the old and the new. For all his eccentricity and arrogance, he had opened another breach in the encircling walls of received truth, and encouraged men to believe that the secrets of nature could be discovered by their own efforts (**40, 41**).

VESALIUS, 1514–1564

One of the most notable contributions of the humanists to science was their restitution of the original texts of Galen, to replace the corrupt versions which had reached medieval Europe through the Arabs. The new editions helped to create that great increase of interest in anatomy which was so marked a feature of the sixteenth century. But although the greatest of the anatomists, Vesalius, began as a follower of Galen, he eventually became a violent opponent of the anatomical writings of his predecessor, and was able to demonstrate and correct many of his errors.

When Vesalius became an exceptionally youthful professor of anatomy at Padua, the greatest medical school of Europe, in 1537, little importance was attached to this ill-paid post. The professor was required to dissect two bodies a year in front of the students, while a treatise dating from 1316 was read out as a commentary on the operation. Vesalius speedily transformed this meaningless ritual into a genuine lesson, taking great pains to make his demonstrations clear and comprehensible. In the process he became increasingly aware that his observations did not tally with Galen's descriptions, and began to question the accuracy of the latter. By 1540 he had realised the truth: Galen's anatomy was based, not on the dissection of the human body, but on the bodies of animals, primarily apes. Vesalius now considered Galen nothing but a fraud, and although his own anatomy remained deeply indebted to him, spared no opportunity to point out his mistakes.

This attitude of defiance towards the great authority on the subject appalled the more conservative of his colleagues, but there was little they could do against the mass of supporting evidence he was able to collect. His message was clear: there could be no reliance on the work of predecessors, and observation and experiment must be the basis of all scientific study of the body. It was through the acceptance of this revolutionary principle that all the advances in anatomy which marked the period were to come about.

In 1543 the publication of Vesalius's great work *De humani corporis fabrica* signalled his triumph over Galen and traditional anatomy. This magnificent folio, with its superb illustrations of the human skeleton, muscles, and organs, supplanted all previous anatomical textbooks. No clearer demonstration of the influence of printing could have been wished for; the ability to reproduce high-quality plates from woodcuts made for a new level of clarity and practicality. The visual emphasis of Renaissance culture, and the enormous strides towards naturalism made by the artists, are similarly represented by the unidentified artist of the *Fabrica*. The book was far from perfect: although many errors had been removed, there were still numerous points at which Vesalius had seen what he expected rather than what was there. And a certain limitation is evident in his outlook: he did not seem particularly interested in identifying special problems in physiology or undertaking detailed researches to illuminate them, being content rather with overall descriptions. Although it was through the study of non-human anatomy that he came to see the pseudo-human nature of Galen's work, he attempted little in the way of comparative anatomy himself (42).

A series of brilliant anatomists soon appeared and continued the work of Vesalius, and men like Fallopio and Coiter began to explore both the details of human anatomy and the possibilities of comparative study with other creatures. Gradually knowledge of the structure and workings of the body was expanded and deepened, by a method of research which was perhaps the most recognisably modern of the time. Unfortunately there were few immediate benefits for practical medicine: here the Paracelsians whom, as believers in the occult, Vesalius would have classed as 'gloomy philosophers', were probably more effective. Only after the chemical discoveries of the eighteenth century was the treatment of disease to make really significant progress. But the anatomical revolution provided one essential component of this future scientific medicine. At the same time it gave a convincing demonstration of the power of critical observation as a scientific method, and encouraged all those in the sixteenth and seventeenth centuries who thought that the moderns could and should advance beyond the ancients (38).

COPERNICUS, 1473–1543

Just as the original texts of Galen had to be restored in the place of corrupt Arab versions, so the astronomical works of Ptolemy were rescued during the Renaissance. The great fifteenth-century German astronomers Feuerbach and Regiomontanus were chiefly responsible for a revival of mathematical astronomy, based on a proper understanding of the Ptolemaic system. But the establishment of a correct text was far from eliminating all the problems, and it became plain that there were inherent deficiencies in the system which could no longer be explained away as the results of errors in transmission. Some of these errors had become more glaring with the passage of thirteen centuries since Ptolemy wrote, during which time a good many observations had been made. The inaccuracy of some of these observations, however, was a problem in itself, and one not immediately recognised by Copernicus and his contemporaries. Since some of the data were faulty, the difficulties in finding a system to accommodate them were much enhanced—in fact no system could have given a satisfactory explanation of them all.

Apart from the purely intellectual interest of their enquiries, the astronomers had good practical reasons for wishing to improve on Ptolemy. To begin with, the general belief in astrology produced a demand for accurate tables of the predicted movements of the planets, to replace the existing and unsatisfactory thirteenth-century compilations. And there was also the question of calendar reform, since, like the planetary tables, the Julian calendar was growing ever more seriously out of step with reality. Copernicus himself was to be consulted by the Papacy on this problem. We might also note that the discoveries made by the explorers of this period to both West and East undermined faith in Ptolemy as a geographer, and perhaps by extension as an astronomer too. But such doubts were confined to the few, and the new mapmakers continued to exploit Ptolemy's popular reputation by putting out new editions of his *Geography* with more correct maps.

To a handful of mathematically proficient astronomers, therefore, it became plain by the end of the fifteenth century that existing attempts to account for the motions of the heavens were inadequate. Copernicus was one of these men, and after studying at Cracow, Bologna, and Padua he returned to his native East Prussia to spend his life as a canon at Frauenberg on the shore of the Baltic. Here, apart from administering the estates of the Cathedral chapter, he worked away at the intractable problems of the skies. A profound traditionalist in most respects, he had set himself a limited and highly technical task, that of improving on Ptolemy's computations of planetary positions. But it was not merely a question of tidying up the mathematics: there was also a particular device employed by his predecessors to which Copernicus had philosophical objections. According to the principles enunciated by the Pythagoreans and adopted by Plato and Aristotle, movement in the heavens was both circular and uniform. It was to preserve the circularity that the devices known as epicycles and eccentrics had been resorted to, but these Copernicus himself was forced to accept, if his system was to work at all. What he did not consider reasonable or proper was a third device called the equant, and he set out to eliminate it from astronomy. The equant had been introduced, on top of the other complications, to allow for the extreme irregularity of the motion of the planets as seen from the earth. Even with all the circles, it was impossible to make their movements uniform about the centre of any of the circles used to compute their orbits. The best that could be done was to relate the motion to some point in the circle which was not its centre, but in relation to which it was consistent. In effect this was a mathematical description of uneven motion in a circle, and Copernicus regarded it as a departure from the basic principles of cosmology.

In order to rid astronomy of the tiresome equant, and to simplify the scheme of the heavens, Copernicus cast around in true sixteenth-century style for help from the authorities. It would appear that he had been much influenced, as a young student in Italy, by the Neo-platonic and Pythagorean notions then becoming current, and it was the astronomers of the latter school who provided him with the required guidance. In a spurious treatise attributed to Plutarch he found descriptions of some alternatives to the geocentric universe. Let Copernicus himself take up the story:

I pondered long upon this uncertainty of mathematical tradition in establishing the motions of the system of the spheres. At last I began to chafe that philosophers could by no means agree on any one theory of the mechanism of the Universe, wrought for us by a supremely good and orderly Creator, although in other respects they investigated with meticulous care the minutest points relating to its circles. I therefore took pains to read again the works of all the philosophers on whom I could lay hand to seek out whether any of them had ever supposed that the motions of the spheres were other than those demanded by the mathematical schools. I found first in Cicero that Hicetas had realised that the Earth moved. Afterwards I found in Plutarch that certain others had held the like opinion. I think fit here to add Plutarch's own words, to make them accessible to all:

'The rest hold the Earth to be stationary, but Philolaus the Pythagorean says that she moves around the fire on an oblique circle like the Sun and Moon. Heraclides of Pontus and Ecphantus the Pythagorean also make the Earth to move, not indeed through

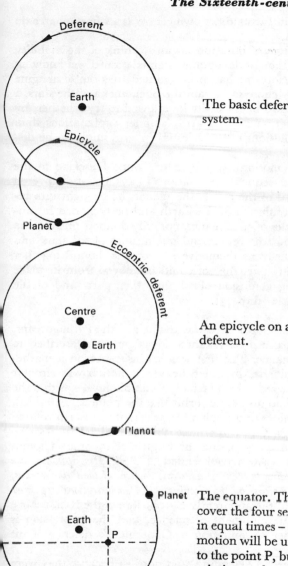

The basic deferent epicycle system.

An epicycle on an eccentric deferent.

The equator. The planet will cover the four sections of its orbit in equal times – therefore its motion will be uniform in relation to the point P, but irregular in relation to the earth.

29

space but by rotating around her own centre as a wheel on an axle from West to East.'

Taking advantage of this I too began to think of the mobility of the Earth; and though the opinion seemed absurd, yet knowing now that others before me had been granted freedom to imagine such circles as they chose to explain the phenomena of the stars, I considered that I also might easily be allowed to try whether, by assuming some motion of the Earth, sounder explanations than theirs for the revolutions of the celestial spheres might so be discovered.

Thus assuming motions, which in my work I ascribe to the Earth, by long and frequent observations I have at last discovered that, if the motions of the rest of the planets be brought into relation with the circulation of the Earth and be reckoned in proportion to the circles of each planet, not only do their phenomena presently ensue, but the orders and magnitudes of all stars and spheres, nay the heavens themselves, become so bound together that nothing in any part thereof could be moved from its place without producing confusion of all the other parts and of the Universe as a whole [**doc. 3**].

It can be said that Copernicus was the heir of the Pythagoreans, for he took as his basic material three ideas generally ascribed to them in the Renaissance. The first was his insistence on a mathematically simple universe, in which heavenly motion was circular and uniform. The second, which he took from Philolaus, was that the Earth moved, and had an annual orbit like the planets. The third, derived from Heraclides and Ecphantus, was that the Earth rotated daily on its own axis. Contemporaries did not hesitate to describe Copernicus as a Pythagorean, and the English astronomer Thomas Digges published in 1576 a book called *A Perfit Description of the Caelestiall Orbes according to the most aunciente doctrine of the Pythagoreans, latelye revived by Copernicus and by Geometricall Demonstrations approved.* So here again we find the apparently esoteric lore of the Renaissance involved with the development of science, and the impression is deepened by a closer examination of Copernicus's defence of his views.

They certainly needed defending, and not just because they were new and shocking to traditionalists. As a mathematical exercise they were none too successful: no worse than Ptolemy, but not significantly better in simplicity or accuracy. For example, although the earth was now in orbit, the sun was not the centre of that orbit, and the reference point for the whole universe was the geometrical point in space which was at that centre—so the system was not truly heliocentric at all. And there was no important reduction in the number of circles required to account for the phenomena, so in this respect too the desired simplicity was still lacking. Where the system did score was in what its author himself called harmony: it had a qualitative simplicity despite the great complexity of its mathematics.

There were two notable irregularities of planetary motion which could only be explained, in a geocentric universe, by the use of epicycles. The first of these was retrograde motion: when a planet appears for a time to move in a westward, rather than the normal eastward direction relative to the fixed stars. In the Copernican universe this occurred when the earth overtook the superior planets, or was overtaken by those nearer the sun, according to their different orbital periods, As it could only occur when the earth was nearest to the planet in question, it also explained why the external or superior planets were most brilliant when in retrograde motion. The second was the apparent irregularity of planetary orbital periods as observed from the earth. They possess a consistent average, but vary substantially on one side or the other every trip, because the earth too is in motion, and is not the centre of their orbit. Both these problems were now explained by the basic structure of the heavens, and not by mathematical fictions.

Similarly Copernicus cleared up the puzzle of the inferior planets, Venus and Mercury. They appeared to take a year, just like the sun, to journey across the fixed stars, and this gave rise to disputes about their relative position. But if they were nearer to the sun, and therefore to the centre of the universe, than to the earth, their periods could be established on a new basis, and it became plain that Mercury was much nearer to the sun. The way in which the two planets never moved far from the sun was also explained quite naturally, and not by the elaborate devices used by Ptolemy to tie their respective motions together.

Unfortunately it was not possible to give a quantitative account of planetary motion to match the admirable economy of this qualitative description, and in order to give reasonably satisfactory predictions of events in the heavens a great many epicycles and eccentrics were still required, so the harmony of the new proposals was much obscured. It needed a great deal of mathematical knowledge, and an open mind, to see the advantages of Copernicus's proposals as put forward in his great work, the *De Revolutionibus Orbium Caelestium*, published in 1543, the same year as Vesalius's *Fabrica*. In a famous passage in the cosmological first book he defended his hypothesis with references to the Neoplatonic cult of the sun, and to another harmony mentioned in the previous quotation. Whereas the Ptolemaic system could allow for wide differences in the size of the planetary orbits, for the Copernican they were determined by the structure of the system as a whole, and could have only one true value. Here is a further short extract from Copernicus's own statement of his case:

> In the middle of all sits Sun enthroned. In this most beautiful temple could we place this luminary in any better position from which he can illuminate the whole at once? He is rightly called the Lamp, the Mind, the Ruler of the Universe: Hermes Trismegistus names him the Visible God, Sophocles' Electra calls him the All-seeing. So the Sun sits as upon a royal throne ruling his children the planets which circle round him. The Earth has the Moon at her service. As Aristotle says, in his *On Animals*, the Moon has the closest relationship with the Earth. Meanwhile the Earth conceives by the Sun, and becomes pregnant with an annual re-birth.
>
> So we find underlying this ordination an admirable symmetry in the Universe, and a clear bond of harmony in the motion and magnitude of the Spheres such as can be discovered in no other wise [**doc. 3**].

There is something of a cheat about this, since the sun was not at the centre of the Copernican system, and much the same thing could be said about most of the general cosmological justifications in the first book—they do not square with the mathematics of the rest. Yet it was because of the mathematics, however imperfect, that the *De Revolutionibus* was so important; no one would ever have taken it seriously without them. As Copernicus himself said, mathematics are for mathematicians, and so was his book.

As far as the layman was concerned, the new hypothesis was hardly likely to have much appeal. It destroyed the conventional picture of the earth as the centre of the universe, and sent it spinning, an insignificant little ball, among the planets. Common sense indicated plainly that if this were to happen, everyone would fall off this dangerous platform, of whose violent movements they could hardly remain unaware. The whole tidy structure of the Aristotelian cosmos would collapse, and what would replace it? Criticism of this kind did not become common until the early seventeenth century, since for a long time few but professional astronomers had much understanding of the new theory. For many of them the wider implications of the change were unacceptable, but the mathematical interest of the most thorough primer of astronomy since Ptolemy was undeniable. As for Copernicus himself, despite the audacity with which he reconstructed the universe in the name of astronomy, he had no desire to attack Aristotelian physics. He put forward a series of notably unconvincing arguments designed to show that things went on just as before in the sublunary region, and that the displacement of the earth made no difference to anything but astronomy. One must sadly conclude that Copernicus was largely unaware of his own achievement. For him the successful attack on the equant meant more than the physical rearrangement of the cosmos.

Professional interest in the new system was enormously enhanced by the publication in 1551 of the *Prutenic Tables*, a new set of calculations of future planetary positions made by Erasmus Reinhold according to the Copernican theory. Although still far from perfect, they were notably better than the three-centuries old tables they replaced, and did much to make the system on which they were based respectable. The work of Copernicus therefore became part of the highly specialised tradition of mathematical astronomy, and gradually its merits and interest were more widely recognised by the practitioners of this art. But most of them preferred to evade the question of the physical reality of the theory, and to treat it simply as a basis for calculation. A process had been started which was only to end with Newton, but the world as a whole was hardly yet aware of its importance [**doc. 3**] (**32, 34**).

TYCHO BRAHE, 1546–1601

It has already been emphasised that there were many inaccuracies in the data with which Copernicus worked, and it must be added that he himself was a feeble observer and made no serious effort to improve the situation. But a Danish nobleman with an obsessive interest in alchemy and astrology was soon to supply the essential addition to the Copernican proposals by raising astronomical observation to new heights of thoroughness and accuracy. In his early youth Tycho Brahe had discovered the inadequacy of even the Prutenic tables, and just as he seemed about to devote all his time to alchemy a startling event in the heavens persuaded him to transfer his attention back to astronomy. This event was the appearance in 1572 of a new star, a nova, in the constellation of Cassopeia. Not only was the newcomer as bright as Jupiter in its early stages, but it seemed to lie in the sphere of the fixed stars, where the Aristotelian cosmology would not allow even the possibility of change. Observers watched it anxiously to see if it would exhibit any parallax—movement against the fixed stars—which would enable them to treat it as a meteorological phenomenon, as comets were also thought to be. But no parallax was to be seen, and while astrologically-minded protestants were interpreting the star as a divine warning of the St. Bartholomew's Day massacres in France, Tycho and other astronomers were inspired to fresh consideration of the nature of the heavens.

Tycho's work on the nova attracted the attention of the King of Denmark, who granted him the feudal lordship of the island of Hveen, where he established his great observational centre named Uraniborg. Using instruments of unprecedented size—the only way to achieve reasonable accuracy before the invention of the telescope—he spent twenty years making observations of the skies. Not only did he work to new limits of accuracy, he also grasped the essential principle that only a sustained series of regular observations could provide a sound basis for mathematical astronomy.

Tycho also developed his own cosmology, although the scheme he chose was also adopted independently by some of his contemporaries. In order to make his conclusions on the nova and the comet of 1577, which he also showed to lie outside the sublunary region, fit in, he was obliged to reject Aristotle. But in other ways he remained a traditionalist, and resorted to an ingenious compromise in order to maintain the earth at the centre of the universe. According to Tycho, the planets revolved around the sun, in the Copernican manner, but the sun was itself in motion around the earth. Mathematically this came to the same thing as a heliocentric universe, but at the cost of a certain untidiness and physical implausibility it also preserved the special position of the earth and allowed the retention of Aristotelian physics without undue strain. There was also a good astronomical reason for this view, because even with his new instruments Tycho was unable to observe any stellar parallax, the movement of the stars relative to one another which would result from the earth's motion. Copernicus had been aware of this difficulty, and was obliged to postulate a very large universe, which would render the parallax so small as to be unobservable. So it was not surprising that Tycho's cosmology enjoyed a certain popularity for a time, but his fame rests far more securely on his observational achievements, and in the hands of Kepler these were to produce the next great advance in theoretical astronomy [**doc. 4**] (**32, 34**).

WILLIAM GILBERT, 1540–1603

The phenomena of magnetic attraction had long been known, and one of the most notable surviving examples of medieval experimental science is the letter on the magnet written by Pierre de Maricourt in 1269. The importance of the compass in navigation, and the increasing demand for precise understanding of the irregularities in its behaviour, encouraged fresh interest in the subject during the Renaissance. At first interest was stronger on the part of natural magicians than on that of scientists, but results of great importance were obtained when the English doctor William Gilbert undertook the series of experiments described in the treatise he published in 1600 under the title *On the Magnet, Magnetick Bodies also, and on the great magnet the Earth: a new Physiology, demonstrated by many arguments and experiments.*

Gilbert was certainly in part a natural magician, and described magnetism as if it were an occult uncontrollable force: he associated it with the *anima* or moving soul of the earth, and then used this belief in an animate universe to strengthen arguments that the earth moved. He was equally interested, as was appropriate for a doctor, in the medical powers attributed to the magnet. But he was above all a very gifted experimenter, and his book can be considered the first great example of the experimental method. It was, however, almost entirely non-mathematical, and in this respect emphasises how the experimental investigation of nature had yet to become properly quantified.

Using small spherical magnets floating in water, Gilbert was able to reinforce deductions from the manner in which lodestones were

35

found in the earth, and to conclude that the earth was a gigantic magnet. He also showed that 'the earth's centre is the centre of the earth's magnetic movements, though magnetic bodies are not borne direct toward the centre in the magnetic movement save when they are attracted by the poles'. Another very important result at which he arrived was the distinction between magnetism and electricity, and in carrying out experiments on the latter he used an electroscope of his own invention. His attempts to improve navigational methods, although ingenious, proved futile, but this hardly diminishes the significance of his work. In particular, he was much admired by both Galileo and Kepler, and the latter took important intuitions from Gilbert's digressions on astronomy. For Gilbert the universe had no centre: every body was independent, possessed of a magnetic force which attracted bodies to its own surface. Despite the shaky logic of this notion, it illustrates the fruitful independence of mind of a scientist who could write:

> We but seldom quote ancient Greek authors in our support, because neither by using greek arguments nor greek words can the truth be demonstrated or elucidated either more precisely or more significantly.

OTHER THINKERS OF THE SIXTEENTH CENTURY

It was not only the scientists who took exception to the tradition of Aristotle: the very foundation of his system, his logic, was subjected to a parallel assault during the Renaissance. After 1530 there were virtually no new editions of the works of the scholastic logicians, men such as Peter of Spain, Buridan, and even Ockham. Their elaborate formalised approach was condemned for its aridity and difficulty, and replaced by methods intended to satisfy the needs of the pupil rather than the teacher.

The first great figure in this educational reform was Rudolph Agricola, and the second Peter Ramus. Judged as logicians neither can be rated exceptionally high, but their innovations are none the less important for that. Ramus, in particular, who missed no opportunity to condemn Aristotle and the Schoolmen, epitomised certain general trends of the Renaissance. He employed simple spatial models, arranged in diagrammatic form, as his basic material. His conception of thought and communication was geometrical, and his books relied on the ability of printers to set out patterns of words. This simplified schoolroom logic can be associated with the movement towards visual symbolism, with developments in the techniques of painting, and with new attitudes towards space. Despite its inferiority to scholastic logic, considered purely intellectually, Ramist logic probably helped to free the universities to some extent from the hold of Aristotelianism, and perhaps encouraged their students to take a more favourable attitude towards other innovations. Although no great mathematician himself, Ramus was enthusiastic enough about the subject to lecture on it—incompetently, even by his own account —and his quantified approach to logic naturally encouraged interest in mathematics. Ramus is important not merely because he was the predecessor of seventeenth-century educational reformers like Comenius, but because he had a direct impact on the intellectual formation of most educated men of the period through his own textbooks and those influenced by him.

An enthusiasm for mathematics was appropriate enough in the sixteenth century, which saw a notable rebirth of interest in the subject for its own sake. The Italian mathematicians Tartaglia and Cardan made some advances towards the introduction of an effective algebraic method and in probability theory. They and other men such as Benedetti and Simon Stevin also attempted to treat some of the outstanding problems of physics mathematically, with mixed results. In ballistics and kinematics, where they were all trying to develop the impetus theory of the scholastics and to mathematise it, their work remained inconclusive if suggestive. The influence of Archimedes, apparent in this endeavour, had more immediate results in Stevin's work on hydrostatics at the end of the century, which was highly successful in a limited field. A further advance was made in algebra when François Viète proposed general rules for notation, a suggestion which was to be taken up by Descartes.

There was also a good deal of activity in natural history and biology, again stimulated by the new possibilities opened up by printing. Men such as Gesner, Rondelet, and Belon produced enormous catalogues of living beings, plausible and implausible. These works were descriptive and uncritical, and showed the need for a more positive and analytical approach. There were also important collections of flora and fauna from the New World, both stimulating and unreliable. In a similar style improved and enlarged herbals added to the doctor's range of medicines, although they still contained a great deal of superstition and folk-belief. In this respect they can be likened to the popular almanacs, chiefly astrological in character, which provided an outlet for vulgarised scientific knowledge, and helped spread awareness of the Copernican hypothesis.

By the end of the sixteenth century educated men were widely aware that the traditional world picture was being assailed from many sides. But as yet this was little matter for rejoicing to most of them: in an age and a society where death, danger and political uncertainty were ever-present realities, change was still shunned rather than sought. Originality was a quality as much disapproved of by most Elizabethans as it is generally admired today. If from a later standpoint this century appears to be poised on the brink of great advances, to those who lived through it the impression was rather that they were constantly on the brink of dissolution, political, intellectual, and moral. Only in the succeeding era were new certainties to replace the old, and to restore the self-confidence which the collapse of the medieval world and its cosmology had so gravely shaken (55).

Part Two

THE
SCIENTIFIC
REVOLUTION

3 The Breakthrough

If the history of science during the first half of the seventeenth century remains the story of isolated individuals in advance of their age, this is a reflection of both the political and intellectual confusion of this period. The Thirty Years War in Germany developed into a general European conflict, which not only absorbed the attentions of national governments, but also helped create an economic recession which increased their difficulties. The war hindered the publication and transmission of scientific results, and interfered with correspondence between scientists. Since it was not a 'total' war in the modern sense, it did not prevent any of these activities, but it certainly rendered them more difficult. England, the only major country to remain outside the European struggle, underwent a profound internal crisis, culminating in civil war, in its place. The prevailing sense of insecurity increased the tendency of rulers to look suspiciously on innovators, unless they had something of immediate practical value to offer. It also sharpened consciousness of religious differences, and therefore tended to encourage repressive biblical fundamentalism on the part of both Catholics and Protestants.

Even if those possessed of power and wealth had been inclined to support scientists, they would not have found it easy to choose among the innumerable pretenders to their bounty. An incomplete intellectual revolution is almost impossible to institutionalise, for no one can be sure of predicting its eventual course. A further series of individual achievements was necessary before anything like a European community of scientists, or a generally acceptable scientific method, could come into being.

MATHEMATICAL ASTRONOMY: KEPLER, 1571–1630

By the end of the sixteenth century it was apparent that all existing astronomical theories were incapable of accomodating the known

41

data, especially the newly accurate information collected by Tycho. By a happy chance the latter, who spent the last years of his life in exile after a quarrel with the new King of Denmark, ended up at the court of the Emperor Rudolf II in Prague. Rudolf was the greatest patron of astrologers and alchemists in Europe, and this rather unorthodox form of support for scientific research had the effect of bringing together Tycho and the younger genius who was to solve so much of the riddle of the skies.

Johannes Kepler had already published an astronomical work in support of Copernicus which contained an important discovery, and on Tycho's death in 1601 he succeeded him as Imperial Mathematicus, his primary obligation in this post being to cast horoscopes for the Emperor. This was an activity Kepler never abandoned during his life, although he considered current astrological practices (including his own) as superstitious nonsense: he still believed in the possibility of a reformed and effective astrology, and wrote copiously on the subject. 'That the sky does something to man is obvious enough', he remarked, ending sadly, 'but what it does specifically remains hidden.' At the same time he was a Pythagorean number-mystic who was ardently convinced of the basic truth of the Copernican system because of the 'harmonies' so dear to its creator.

His first discovery, published in the *Mysterium Cosmographicum* of 1596, was that the planes of the planetary orbits pass through the sun. This cleared up a number of minor problems which had troubled Copernicus, and was but one of the many new harmonies that Kepler was able to attribute to a heliocentric universe.

Kepler was certainly a very strange person: misanthropic, excitable, oversensitive to imagined slights, and holding beliefs which now seem irrational and unscientific. But at the same time he was an obsessively hard worker, addicted to mathematical calculation almost for its own sake, and unwilling to accept anything short of a perfect result. Much of this extraordinary mixture of qualities comes over in his writings, which contain passages of great penetration and lucidity alongside others which are baffling and abstruse. His own words are apt: 'The roads by which men arrive at their insights into celestial matters seem to me almost as worthy of wonder as those matters in themselves' (**34**). At other times he revealed his Pythagoreanism in passages which resemble better-known comments by Galileo and Newton:

Why waste words? Geometry existed before the Creation, is co-eternal with the mind of God, is God himself (what exists in God that is not God himself?): geometry provided God with a model for the Creation and was implanted into man, together with God's own likeness—and not merely conveyed to his mind through the eyes.

My aim is to show that the heavenly machine is not a kind of divine, live being, but a kind of clockwork (and he who believes that a clock has a soul, attributes the maker's glory to the work), insofar as nearly all the manifold motions are caused by a most simple, magnetic and material force, just as all motions of the clock are caused by a simple weight. And I also show how these physical causes are to be given numerical and geometrical expression (**34**).

As his reference to 'magnetic' force indicates, Kepler took Gilbert's ideas as a basic element of his new cosmology, and we shall see how important this was. But his first two laws were the immediate result of painstaking work on Mars, a planet whose nearness to the earth made its movements particularly difficult to account for. As a good Pythagorean, he was sure that the orbit was a circle, although he recognised that it must be an eccentric circle which did not centre precisely on the sun. He cleared away the whole clutter of epicycles, at the cost of reintroducing the equant, and departing from the uniform motion so treasured by Copernicus.

In all this there was one ultimate consideration: Kepler was determined that his explanations should possess not only mathematical accuracy, but also physical plausibility. Treating the sun as the centre and moving force of the universe, he saw that the speed of a planet's motion could reasonably be expected to vary with its distance from the sun. But even with this departure from accepted dogma, he was still unable to make a circular orbit fit with the figures—a tiresome discrepancy remained, even though it was so small that it would not have worried any previous astronomer. Kepler, however, would not compromise:

For us, who by divine kindness were given such an observer as Tycho Brahe, for us it is fitting that we should acknowledge this divine gift and put it to use. . . . For, if I had believed that we could ignore those eight minutes, I would have patched up my hypothesis accordingly (**34**).

43

Having started out all over again, Kepler began by developing his early intuition that the speed of a planet varied with its distance from the sun, and in the process discovered his Second Law. This is, briefly stated, that the orbital speed of each planet varies in such a manner that a line joining the planet to the sun sweeps through equal areas of the orbit in equal time. It may be added that Kepler made a series of errors in calculation which only cancelled themselves out by luck, and that he continued to use his earlier and inferior inverse-distance law interchangeably with the new one to the end of his life. Even when he had formulated the Second Law, he needed another four years to find an orbit which would work, trying various kinds of ovals before he finally hit on the ellipse. This slowness was surprising, since he was using ellipses on the model of Appollonios's *Conics* to assist in constructing his ovals.

But eventually he arrived at his First Law: the planets move in simple elliptical paths, and the sun occupies one of the two foci of each elliptical orbit. For the first time a single geometrical figure and a simple speed law permitted the description of the planetary system in a manner which could easily be thought of as having physical reality, and which gave accurate predictions of planetary positions. If it took a long time—at least half a century—for the importance of Kepler's discoveries to be fully and widely realised, this is a commentary both on the obscurity with which he presented them and the inadequate diffusion of new scientific discoveries at this period.

That his discovery was not unknown, but produced perplexity as well as interest, is shown by a letter written to the English mathematician Thomas Harriot in 1611 by one of his circle, Sir William Lower:

> For this theorie I am much in love with these particulars: . . . 2°
> His elliptical iter planetarum, for me thinks it shews a Way to the solving of the unknown walks of comets. For as his Ellipsis in the Earths motion is more a circle and in Mars is more longe and in some of the other planets may be longer againe so in thos commets that are appeared fixed the ellipsis may be neere a right line. . . .
> But in his books I am much out of love with thes particulars.
> 1. First his manie and intollerable atechnies, whence derive those manie and vncertaine assayes of calculation. . . .

But despite the obscurities, it is so attractive that he can hardly sleep at night for thinking not of his causes for I cannot phansie those magnetical natures. But aboute his theorie which me thinks (although I cannot yet overmaster manie of his particulars) he establisheth soundlie and as you say overthrowes the circular Astronomie.

His concern for the physical reality of his system led Kepler into a development of Gilbert's theories which anticipated Newton. He believed that the earth, the sun and the planets were all large magnets, and that the sun carried the planets round as it rotated on its own axis by means of rays of a moving force, the *anima motrix*. This force was necessary because he thought of inertia as the tendency of a body to stay put, and therefore had to explain why the planets should move at all. The elliptical orbits he explained by the successive attraction and repulsion between the magnetic poles of the planets and the solar magnet, which produced variable velocities in proportion to their distance from the sun.

Although he did not arrive at the conception of forces as impersonal and inanimate entities, and continued to attribute a degree of purposive intelligence to the universe, Kepler had assembled all the evidence on which this further step could be taken. Apart from the difficulty of such a radical break with previous notions, he was in any case primarily interested in discovering the mathematical harmonies which underlay the scheme of God's universe, and continued to work on these. His chief project was to relate the distances between the planetary orbits to the five regular solids, these last being arranged in a kind of interlocking nest. It almost seemed to work, and Kepler pursued this chimera with the same obstinate singlemindedness as he had the orbit of Mars. In the process he stumbled on his Third Law, which stated that the squares of the times taken by any two planets to describe their orbits are proportional to the cubes of their mean distances from the sun. This law indicated that there was a previously undetected regularity in the planetary system, but otherwise its importance was not immediately obvious; it was to be a vital clue for Newton's theory of gravity. Meanwhile Kepler worked on, discovering other harmonies about which he could rhapsodise, and in particular those which related the universe to the musical scale:

The heavenly motions are nothing but a continuous song for several voices (perceived by the intellect, not by the ear): a music which, through discordant tensions . . . progresses towards certain pre-designed, quasi-six-voiced clausuras, and thereby sets land-marks in the immeasurable flow of time.

We might well ask by what strange chance this mixture of Py-thagorean number-mysticism and belief in a semi-animate universe produced some of the greatest scientific discoveries of all time. Al-though there can be no final answer to such a question, Kepler him-self provides a partial one. Speaking of the English alchemist and Rosicrucian Robert Fludd, with whom he had a bitter controversy, he commented:

> It is obvious that he derives his main pleasure from unintelligible charades about the real world, whereas my purpose is, on the con-trary, to draw the obscure facts of nature into the bright light of knowledge. His method is the business of alchemists, hermetists, and Paracelsians, mine is the task of the mathematician (34).

Kepler dealt in musical and mathematical analogies as Fludd also did, but he knew that his own analogies were exact ones of propor-tion between two systems each having a constant unit of measure-ment, whereas Fludd's were merely based on an identity of number between systems having no other mathematical characteristic in common. It was because he tempered the intuitions of a mystic with the skill of a mathematician that Kepler stands out among the astronomers of his generation [**doc. 4**] (*32, 34*).

Two other aspects of Kepler's work must be mentioned. In the 1620s he employed his new cosmology to prepare a completely fresh set of planetary tables based on the data he had inherited from Tycho. The publication of the *Rudolphine Tables* in 1627 would have earned him European fame quite apart from his other achievements, and these tables remained the standard reference work for astrono-mers for a whole century. And in the middle of his work on Mars, in 1604, he had also published a treatise on optics, in which he established many of the basic principles of geometrical optics. Al-though he did not arrive at a complete law of refraction, he posed the problem properly for the first time. He also explained the working of the human eye as an optical instrument. In a second work, the *Dioptics* of 1611, he worked out the theory of the telescope, newly introduced into astronomy by Galileo, and of the lenses and object glasses used in it.

TELESCOPIC ASTRONOMY: GALILEO, 1564–1642

While Kepler did make telescopic observations, his achievements in this direction could not compare with those of his Italian contemporary Galileo.

Like Tycho before him, Galileo began his career as a serious astronomer (he was already an accomplished mathematician and physicist) by observing a nova, that of 1604. Already a Copernican, he was confirmed in his views by the absence of parallax which placed the new body among the stars, although he kept his opinions for his lectures as Professor of Mathematics at the university of Padua, unlike Kepler who rushed into print as usual with *De Stella Nova* (1606). But his real contribution to astronomy came when he heard of the invention of the telescope in Holland, constructed one for himself, and used it to survey the heavens. He was not the first to do so. Thomas Harriot had made maps of the moon in the summer of 1609, before Galileo made his telescope. But when he published his little book *The Starry Messenger* in 1610 Galileo was able to describe a number of startling discoveries made with a much improved instrument. He began with a familiar body which showed a new aspect:

> The surface of the moon is not perfectly smooth, free from inequalities and exactly spherical, as a large school of philosophers considers with regard to the moon and other heavenly bodies, but that, on the contrary, it is full of irregularities, uneven, full of hollows and protruberances, just like the surface of the earth itself, which is varied everywhere by lofty mountains and deep valleys.

In other words, the difference between the celestial and terrestial regions was less obvious than it should have been, by orthodox Aristotelian theory.

The telescope also showed a host of new stars: the Milky Way, for instance, could now be seen to be composed of innumerable stars, too small and too closely packed to be distinguished with the naked eye. The same was true of the nebulae, and in addition there were new stars to be seen in familiar constellations. The Copernican claim that the universe must be very large, or even infinite as some had begun to speculate, seemed much more reasonable in consequence. And as the stars appeared no bigger through the telescope than they did to the eye, it was evident that they were a long way away, and at the same time that they need not be thought unreasonably large.

Most impressive evidence of all, Galileo found that the moon was not the only planetary satellite: he saw four small bodies very close to Jupiter, which were plainly in orbit around the planet. This at once destroyed much of the remaining strength of the traditional position by showing that the earth could not be the common centre for all the heavens, and provided a model in miniature of the Copernican universe, with a heavenly body surrounded by its own 'planets'. This discovery had an immediate impact not only on the scientists but also on educated men in general, and made Galileo a European celebrity. His gifts as a publicist are undeniable: he is usually considered one of the founders of modern Italian prose style, and there could be no greater contrast than that between his clear, factual booklet of a mere twenty-four pages and Kepler's voluminous baroque obscurities. Kepler himself was fascinated by Galileo's discoveries, and the two men reopened a correspondence begun many years previously. It did not, unhappily, prove a fruitful co-operation, although Kepler was encouraged to make a telescope of his own, and also to develop his work on optics (**34**). Galileo clung obstinately to the Copernican, not the Keplerian, scheme of the universe, considering circles to be the only possible form of heavenly motion. He was not a theoretical astronomer, and his importance in the history of the science derives from his observations—and his trial.

None of the observational evidence rapidly accumulated by Galileo and the many other astronomers who began to employ telescopes constituted a direct proof that the sun was the centre of the planetary system. But two further discoveries made it seem even more probable that such was the case. The first was the identification of sunspots: Galileo was able to show, not merely that these moved with the axial rotation of the sun, but that they were constantly changing their shapes, and were of the nature of 'vapours, or exhalations, or clouds of fumes'. Even the divine sun, it appeared, was not exempt from change.

More significant still, Galileo discovered that Venus possessed phases, like those of the moon, and must therefore be assumed to circle the sun. This had been predicted by Copernican astronomers: now the telescope had confirmed their opinions, and the psychological effect was very considerable. It was impossible for anyone to take the original Ptolemaic theory seriously any longer: if it was to survive at all extensive modifications were needed to accommodate the new evidence. Gradually astronomers moved over to the Copernican viewpoint, and by the middle of the century it was difficult to find serious workers who clung to the old scheme. The telescope also became a popular diversion, and spread general awareness that the heavens were not quite as unguided sense impressions might suggest.

Galileo's notoriety had now become such that it began to attract unfavourable attention from the Catholic Church. After his *Letter to the Grand Duchess Christina* of 1615, in which he trespassed on theological ground to argue the compatibility of Copernicanism and scripture, his position was uncomfortably exposed, although this little polemical tract circulated only in manuscript. The Inquisition took the matter up in 1616, and declared the opinion that the sun was the centre of the universe 'foolish and absurd, philosophically false and formally heretical'. But they only required certain minor corrections in Copernicus's book, making it clear that its hypotheses need not have physical reality, to allow its reissue. Galileo received an admonition not to hold or defend Copernican opinions, which was mild enough under the circumstances. He was rash enough to defy this with his *Dialogue on the Two Chief Systems of the World* in 1632: the Aristotelian case was put forward by a character named Simplicio, who was ridiculed at every turn. Galileo's pretence that he was presenting both systems for the reader to choose freely between them was patently insincere, and the Pope was furious at this disobedience.

In 1633 the Inquisition censured Galileo after a brief hearing, banned the *Dialogue*, and placed him under (comfortable) house arrest. He was no martyr; he had certainly behaved badly and broken his own solemn undertakings, and he was able to continue his scientific work. But the attitude of the Inquisitors was foolish and backward-looking, and as might have been expected served as propaganda both for the enemies of Rome and the supporters of the Copernican system. The trial is an important landmark in the history of science, but its significance should not be exaggerated. Catholic astronomers could work on quite happily, as long as they included saving clauses to the effect that their work was hypothetical. And Galileo's telescopic discoveries were a much better advertisement for the sun-centred universe than his stiff-necked advocacy of a Copernicanism whose inaccuracy had already been demonstrated and corrected by Kepler [**doc. 5**] (**34, 45**).

GALILEO'S PHYSICS

The reason Galileo clung to a Copernican theory in which the planets moved in circles, even after Kepler's work, was however a vital part of his great contribution to theoretical science. Determined to show that the physical motion of the earth was not merely possible but natural, and that Aristotelian arguments against it based on terrestrial physics were devoid of meaning, he turned the tradition of medieval dynamics upside down. Instead of beginning with the assumption that all bodies had a natural 'place' in the universe, and explaining their movements by their desire to return to it, Galileo set out to analyse their actual behaviour in mathematical terms. There can be no doubt that he was deeply influenced by the Platonic notions so widespread in his time, as a famous passage in his *The Assayer* (1623) shows:

> Philosophy is written in this grand book, the universe, which stands continually open to our gaze. But the book cannot be understood unless one first learns to comprehend the language and read the letters in which it is composed. It is written in the language of mathematics, and its characters are triangles, circles, and other geometric figures without which it is humanly impossible to understand a single word of it: without these, one wanders about in a dark labyrinth.

And elsewhere in the same book he developed this insight further:

> To excite in us tastes, odours, and sounds I believe that nothing is required in external bodies except shapes, numbers, sizes, and slow or rapid movements.

Geometrised motion was the keynote of Galileo's new cosmology, in the true Platonic tradition. Since he believed the world to be finite, he necessarily conceived the motion of its constituent parts to be circular: 'If all integral bodies in the world are by nature movable, or anything else but circular.' On the basis of this erroneous postulate he not only advocated circular planetary orbits in a heliocentric universe, but also constructed a new conceptual framework for the physical sciences. Not only did the earth move, but all bodies in the universe were in motion unless there was something to stop them. The apparent immobility of objects on the earth was a case of a local inertial system:

That motion which is common to many moving things is idle and inconsequential to the relation of these movables among themselves, nothing being changed among them: and that is operative only in the relation that they have with other bodies lacking that motion, among which their location is changed.

Although Galileo spoke of horizontal planes on which, if there were no accelerating or retarding causes, a body would continue to move at a uniform velocity, these horizontal planes were spherical surfaces having the centre of the earth for their centre. He did not, therefore, formulate the law of inertia properly, and it was left for Newton to reveal the true unity of celestial and terrestrial physics, which Galileo's obsession with circularity had partially obscured. But probably it was only through this mistaken notion that he was able to make the necessary intuitive leap, a good illustration of the kind of zig-zags by which science often progresses. In practical terms the sphericity of the horizontal planes made no difference to the results Galileo obtained in treating problems of mechanics and dynamics. Their radius at the earth's surface was so large that they could be discounted for any projectile known to him, and its motion treated as if it were in a straight line. His failure to state the law of inertia properly was therefore not crucial for his physics, however erroneous it rendered his cosmology.

In common sense terms Galileo's new approach could only seem absurd. Objects thrown or dropped into the air do not describe any motions that are either circular or parallel to the earth's surface; their only regular motion is that of free fall, as Aristotle had known. In order to arrive at his new position, Galileo had adopted a thoroughgoing idealist or abstractionist standpoint. He knew very well that he was disregarding the complexities of the real situation in order to reveal the fundamental laws they obscured. This step once taken, 'facts which at first sight seem improbable will, even on scant observation, drop the cloak which has hidden them and stand forth in naked and simple beauty'.

It would be novel indeed if computations and rates made in abstract numbers should not thereafter correspond to concrete gold and silver coins and merchandise. Do you know what does happen, Simplicio? Just as the computer who wants his calculations to deal with sugar, silk and wool must discount the boxes, bales and other packings, so the philosopher geometrician, when he wants to recognise in the concrete, the effects which he has proved in the abstract, must deduct the material hindrances, and if he is able to do so, I assure you that things are in no less agreement than arithmetical computations. The errors, then, lie not in the abstractness or concreteness, not in the geometry or physics, but in a calculator who does not know how to make a true accounting.

There was a truly Platonic paradox in the conception of a basic structure of the world which possessed reality only in the abstract.

If the inspiration for Galileo's great conceptual leap was Platonist, he dealt with the practical problems it raised by methods which were Aristotelian in origin. His teachers at Padua had introduced him to the corpus of problems in dynamics and kinematics associated with the fourteenth-century scholastics, and he adapted their logical and geometrical techniques to his new needs. He began with the classic problem of finding a mathematical expression for the behaviour of bodies falling under the influence of gravity. He considered the question in a purely kinematic form, postponing any discussion of the nature of gravity until he could give a precise account of its effects. He reproaches his Aristotelian mouthpiece:

> You err, Simplicio, for you should rather have said that everyone knows that this cause is *called* gravity. Now, I am not asking you for the names, but for the very essence of this matter. Apart from the name given to it, which has become familiar by usage . . . we know no more about the virtue causing a stone to drop . . . than we do about the virtue tending to keep a projectile aloft or about the virtue which guides the moon on its orbit.

Galileo did not realise that all these phenomena involve the operation of gravity! The elimination of questions of causation was followed by the discovery of the fundamental law that the distances covered by a falling body are to each other as the squares of the times ($s = \frac{1}{2}at^2$). He did not, however, claim that bodies of different weight would fall at the same speed: this would only be true in a vacuum, whose possible existence he asserted against Aristotle's denial. Galileo dropped no weights from the Leaning Tower of Pisa, since he knew very well that if they were markedly different they would not arrive at the ground simultaneously. But the difference would not be in proportion to their density:

The variation of speed observed in bodies of different specific gravities is not caused by the difference in specific gravity but depends on external circumstances and, in particular, upon the resistance of the medium, so that if this is removed all bodies would fall with the same velocity.

One of the few experiments Galileo actually stated that he had carried out was rolling a metal ball down an inclined plane to test the law, and he claimed to have obtained a confirmatory result which was probably in reality only very approximate. While he was an exceptionally talented and ingenious experimenter, he did not carry out many experiments which related directly to his greatest discoveries: he had a surprising and sometimes excessive faith in the accuracy of his purely theoretical formulations. Many of the experiments he describes or suggests are 'thought experiments' he never actually attempted. It remains true, of course, that his theories could be empirically tested, if sufficiently accurate methods of measurement could be devised, and that other scientists were soon to make up for his relative indifference to this form of proof.

Having arrived at the law of free fall, Galileo was able to combine it with his approximate conception of inertia, and give the first satisfactory explanation of the behaviour of projectiles. A body thrown on a horizontal plane, without any obstacle, would remain in uniform motion indefinitely, but in practice, 'it will add to the first uniform and indestructible motion the downward propensity which it has because of gravity'.

This compound motion would appear as a parabola, although this trajectory would also be liable to variation on account of air resistance. Again this was not an easy theory to test, and Galileo did not possess the mathematical knowledge necessary to construct the curves actually described by projectiles. But the method of calculation, by the combination of uniform horizontal motion and naturally accelerated falling motion, was correct, even if both the theory and its application were still not completely accurate. Among several interesting conclusions he drew was one that 'the velocities acquired by a body in falling on differently inclined planes are equal'.

He argued that he had proved both this and his notion of the conservation of momentum by observing the motion of the pendulum. This was not precisely true, but his introduction of the pendulum into physics laid the foundations for the later concept of kinetic energy. He used Mersenne's discovery that the square of the period of vibration varied with the length of the thread. The pendulum was to become an important factor in scientific research, and one of Galileo's last suggestions was that it should be used for the regulation of clocks (he himself used a kind of water clock in his experiments).

Another important initiative taken by Galileo was in developing the study of the strength of materials. His conclusions were in error, and had any builders or engineers followed his calculations they would have had some unpleasant surprises, for he seriously over-estimated the strength of beams and other structures. But the principles on which he worked were largely correct, and provided a basis for later and more successful assaults on the problem. Neither this nor Galileo's astronomical work, however, can be compared in importance with the revolution he effected in the physics of moving bodies. He had fused his Platonic insights into the mathematical nature of the phenomena with the Aristotelian and Archimedean tradition he had learned from his Paduan and Pisan masters, and made a crucial breakthrough. It remained for others to perceive and exploit the full consequences of his achievement, both by conducting systematic experiments to extend its application, and by making it part of a cosmology which would include an accurate description of planetary motion [**docs. 5, 6**] (**44, 45, 46**).

4 The New Philosophy

THE SCIENTIFIC COMMUNITY

While no accurate figure can ever be given, the number of people seriously interested in science in the Europe of 1600 was very small, probably no more than a few thousands, and many of these were interested rather than active. Scientists had few formal means of contact, unless they were members of a progressive university such as Padua, and many of them worked in isolation. But there was an increasing consciousness of the need for speedy communication of new discoveries, and many researchers began to correspond with one another. The French friar Marin Mersenne (1588–1648) built up a network of correspondents which included Galileo and Hobbes as well as most of the important French scientists of the day. Gradually a European scientific community was being formed, and there can be little doubt that this new-found group solidarity encouraged men to be bolder in their speculations, at least in private correspondence.

Small circles of scientists, such as the group sponsored by Northumberland and Ralegh, or the Lyncean Academy to which Galileo belonged, had begun to appear by the turn of the century. In England the trend was advanced by the benefaction of the great Elizabethan merchant Sir Thomas Gresham, who was responsible for the foundation of Gresham College in London in 1596. He endowed seven professorships, whose holders lived in what had been his mansion house, and were obliged to give public lectures. Three of the chairs were scientific and the college swiftly became a centre for scientists. It was associated with Gilbert's work on magnetism, the development of logarithms, advances in mapmaking, the invention of the slide rule, and other mathematical, astronomical, and technological activities.

The establishment of these groups, and others like them, did not have immediate and revolutionary consequences for the growth of science. The able but limited scientists who made up their membership were already able to put their knowledge to practical use, and to reduce the great areas of ignorance which still surrounded them.

They also contributed to the formation of a wide public interest in science as a means to direct control over man's environment. Their discussions and experiments revealed with a new clarity the scope and nature of the problems still awaiting solution, and in this way represented a step towards resolving them. But the meeting of scientists on a new co-operative basis could not in itself eliminate the inconsistencies and false conceptions which were still so much present in the general theories of the structure of the world which underlay their work.

The appearance of a scientific community gave an enormous additional impetus to scientific activity; it produced a host of small but significant discoveries and advances, and above all it created an audience which would be receptive to any new ideas. After about 1630 there was little chance of any important theoretical or practical contribution to science going unrecognised for long, and this made for a great intensification of the search for a satisfactory alternative to the evidently outmoded system of Aristotle. In the new atmosphere of enthusiasm and open-mindedness any new system-makers were assured of a sympathetic hearing (**58**).

FRANCIS BACON, 1561–1626

His immediate contemporaries knew Bacon best as a successful lawyer who rose to the position of Lord Chancellor and the title of Lord Verulam and Viscount St Albans before he was disgraced in 1621 for taking bribes. But within a very short time his posthumous fame as a writer on scientific subjects equalled anything he had achieved as lawyer or statesman. Bacon was not entirely a progressive thinker: in astronomy, for instance, he preferred the Tychonic system to that of Copernicus, let alone Kepler, Nor was he a great scientist: he dabbled in experiment, but made no discoveries. But his fame was justified: he was a superb writer, with a great gift for the telling phrase, and a man of remarkable vision. Bacon saw that Aristotelianism was dead, and that a new science was taking its place. He entertained the most far-reaching hopes for 'the relief of man's estate' by the application of his new scientific method, following the good example of the 'mechanical arts'. 'Now the true and lawful goal of the sciences is none other than this: that human life be endowed with new discoveries and powers.'

The discoveries Bacon anticipated would not be entirely new, for he shared the belief of the Renaissance magicians in a golden age before the Fall, to which mankind must seek to return. Similarly he used the alchemical principle of 'reduction' as the pattern for his attempts to identify the 'natures' of different substances. But although he shared the desire of the natural magicians for power and control over the universe, Bacon was highly critical of the methods and attitudes of most such men. While the ends of astrology, magic and alchemy were noble, their practitioners had no serious idea of how to attain them. Their intellectual inadequacy and laziness meant that they never made any significant progress, and by failing to co-operate and allow any sort of cumulative knowledge to evolve they perperpetually fell into the same elementary errors. What Bacon himself proposed was a commonsense version of their projects, informed by a legalistic, organising mind and directed to a pragmatic, realistic end.

Convinced as he was that the magicians had erred, not in their basic conception of the world as a highly complex assembly of interacting systems, but in their obsession with easy answers, Bacon placed his faith in his inductive method. He championed planned experiment and systematic research as the pathway to new knowledge. He wrote:

> There are and can be only two ways of searching into and discovering truth. The one flies from the senses and particulars to the most general axioms, and from these principles, the truth of which it takes for settled and immovable, proceeds to judgment and the discovery of middle axioms. And this way is now in fashion. The other derives axioms from the senses and particulars, rising by a gradual and unbroken ascent, so that it arrives at the most general axioms last of all. This is the true way, but as yet untried(1).

Because all previous attempts to construct a general system based on a few simple premises had failed, he condemned such exercises in deductive logic as futile.

With the advantage of hindsight we can see that Bacon was simultaneously right and wrong. The world was perhaps even more complex than he thought, and certainly the full understanding of its structure far more difficult than he ever imagined, yet the great steps forward came from just the kind of intuitive leaps in the dark

C*

that he deplored. Bacon failed to understand that scientific experiments and theories must eventually be mathematical, and that general systems based on mathematical principles would provide the essential framework for purposive scientific experiment. It is because he combined such insight into the errors of others, and such a grasp of many essential problems, with this blindness to the greatest problem of all, that he now seems such an enigmatic figure. Although Bacon's plan for a great programme of scientific research was misconceived, his influence was still great, and the English scientists of the seventeenth century came to think of him, quite rightly, as the prophet of the new science. The existence of such an intellectual champion, however wrong-headed many of his ideas were, helped both to make science respectable and to stimulate others into thinking about its methodology (**56, 63**).

DESCARTES, 1596–1650

To an even greater degree than most other scientists of the age, the French thinker René Descartes began his career as a philosopher and mathematician. In both fields he made contributions of outstanding importance, quite apart from his general cosmological theories. In mathematics he was chiefly notable for the development of co-ordinate geometry, the first really great advance beyond the techniques known to the ancients. By a combination of the analytical method and the application of algebra to geometry he showed how the position of a point in a plane could be determined by its distance from two fixed lines. He did not perfect this method, probably because it did not prove of very much use in the development of his physical ideas. For despite Descartes's gifts as a mathematician, it was rather from the standpoint of his philosophical arguments that he chose to tackle scientific problems. He is generally considered the first truly modern philosopher, the founder of an approach which has served as the basis of almost all subsequent philosophy. The radical nature of his thought was evident in the first principle with which he began: that of all-embracing doubt. Having resolved to doubt everything he possibly could, Descartes narrowed down the range of what could certainly be known until he arrived at his famous *cogito*: 'I think, therefore I am.' By concentrating on the act of knowing rather than on what is known he introduced a new subjectivism into philosophy, and formulated a set of problems which have provided the central concerns of his successors to the present day.

Just as in philosophy Descartes set out to overthrow the doctrines of the past, and replace them with a system based on one original logical statement, so he also sought to reveal the true nature of the world. Here his starting-point was a definition of matter as 'extension', that is, it constitutes space and is identified with it. Now in a sense this is certainly a geometrical conception, and Descartes wanted to unite mathematics and natural science. He also aimed to transfer the methods of thought of mathematics, such as deduction from axioms and algebraic calculation, into the natural sciences. He was so convinced of the universal applicability of his method that he believed it possible to establish the whole general plan of a new and true cosmology in one lifetime, merely leaving some details for others to fill in. This confidence may seem ridiculous to us, but it produced the first comprehensive world picture which could really challenge that of Aristotle for both range and plausibility.

Subjectivism was important for Cartesian natural science. It allowed a distinction between the mathematical structure of the universe and the widely varying ways in which it is perceived by men. Colour, taste, smell, hardness and other physical properties could be treated as subjective reactions to contact with particular bits of space, and therefore not 'scientific' in the same sense as the basic structure. It was sufficient for an explanation of the world to arrive at a logical and axiomatic physics, which would be a description of the behaviour of moving forms of space. Descartes wrote triumphantly at the end of his *Principles of Philosophy* (1644):

Thus I can demonstrate by a very easy reckoning that there is no phenomenon in nature whose explanation has been omitted from this treatise. For there is nothing to be included among these phenomena, but what we can perceive by means of our senses. And except for the motion, size, shape and situation of the parts of each body, which I have explained here as exactly as I could, we perceive nothing external to ourselves by means of our senses save light, colours, odours, tastes, sounds, and the sense of touch. Of all these also I have proved that we perceive nothing outside of our own thoughts, except the motions, sizes and shapes of certain bodies. So that I have proved that there is nothing at all in this

59

visible world, in so far as it is merely visible or perceptible, beyond the things I have accounted for.

The rejection of sense experience could never be anything but illusory: only through the senses could it be decided whether the abstract constructions of mathematical physics gave a satisfactory explanation of the phenomena. As we shall see, Descartes's ingenious theories did not do so, and he never made a serious attempt to test them; seduced by the logical beauty of his ideas, he became blind to the possibility that they might be wrong.

Starting with the concept of matter as extension in space, it was necessary to explain how this matter was divided up and how local motion could occur in the universe. One logical consequence of the definition was that there could be no vacuum, because this would be a contradiction of the basic premise of the system. Similarly, matter had to be infinitely divisible, and an atomic theory was therefore excluded, although there are some superficial resemblances between atomism and Cartesian physics. The latter did employ particles, but they were not the only constituent of the universe. Matter existed in three orders of magnitude: the coarse particles which composed the earth and the planets, and were opaque, the fine particles which formed the sky and transmitted light, and the plastic, non-particulate substance which filled the interstices between the particles and was the source of light. In this densely packed universe, any motion had to involve the displacement of neighbouring bodies, and particle was constantly hitting particle, provoking unending rearrangements. It followed that the quantity of motion in the universe, or the sum of all the products of mass and velocity, had to remain constant.

The existence of motion under such conditions would, Descartes was convinced, produce a series of vortices. The solar system was a case in point, and the universe was composed of a series of similar vortices, interlocking like soap-bubbles. In the vortex the fine particles were the essential agents: their centrifugal force pushed the plastic light-matter to the centre, to form the sun, or the fixed stars which were each at the centre of an independent system. The coarse matter formed the solid bodies which were carried round in the movement of the vortex. This gross earthly matter was inert, and it was only because it was mixed with quantities of the other two orders that there was any motion on earth. Terrestrial physics therefore became an analysis of the way in which the lighter particles and the light-matter pushed around these heavier particles. Gravity, for instance, was explained by the tendency of fast-moving particles to push down any earthly matter that would give way to them. In fact the theory seemed to explain everything, and Descartes was even equal to such intractable problems as that of magnetism. He postulated the existence of two sets of screw-like particles, one with a left-hand thread and the other with a right-hand thread, following a circular path round the earth, then travelling down screwed channels through the centre of the earth.

Not only were such flights of the imagination constantly taking the place of verifiable physical theories in the work of Descartes, but his system did not really include any mathematics. Although the method was based on mathematical principles, few of the conclusions were capable of being tested by measurement. And when Huygens, at first a great enthusiast for Descartes, investigated the seven rules given by his master for the crucial case of the impact of two bodies, he discovered that only the first of them was correct. Compared with Cartesian natural philosophy, that of Aristotle is a triumph of common sense and intellectual honesty.

Yet the aims of Descartes were to serve as an inspiration for his successors, whatever the failings of his own attempt to fulfil them. The 'mechanical philosophy', which sought to explain nature by means of mathematical and mechanical concepts alone, was to dominate scientific thought from this time onwards. The picture of the universe as a vast collection of small bodies acting constantly on one another by physical contact, or the corpuscularean theory as it came to be called, would eventually lead to the discovery of a natural world far more complex than even Descartes's fertile imagination could have anticipated. But in the meantime his wrongheaded and arrogant pretence that he had revealed the basic structure of the world was of immense service, for it stimulated others to succeed, little by little, where he had failed in the grand manner.

It was in physics that it proved possible to correct Descartes's errors and build on his insights. Other subjects which were equally a part of his cosmology gained less; his chemical theories, for instance, were of little use to anyone. But in physiology his mechanistic approach raised important issues, even if it did not provoke immediate and startling discoveries. He tried to explain the functioning of the body in crudely mechanistic terms, supposing the nervous system to be formed of tiny tubes carrying a 'vital fluid'. By virtue of this communications system the animal body became an assembly of reflexes, activated by stimuli received from the environment. Once more Descartes's intuition was correct in principle, but he was completely unable to give a convincing explanation of how things worked in practice. Only after many further developments in physics and chemistry would it be possible to describe the nervous system accurately. But the idea that the life of animals could be explained in mechanistic terms, and did not require the existence of some kind of soul, lay behind much of the significant work in physiology from the late seventeenth century onwards.

The absence of a soul, considered as a necessary part of the organism, posed serious philosophical problems. For animals it was easy enough. Descartes simply treated them as living machines, whose actions could be predicted in their entirety. But for human beings the dualisms between mind and body and free will and determinism had both theological and practical implications. Descartes tried to evade these by arguing that although the soul could not alter the total quantity of movement in the universe, it could alter its direction. Within a very short time the discovery of the law of the conservation of momentum, according to which the total quantity of movement in any given direction is constant, had rendered this argument futile. The problem of the relation between mind and matter could not be solved by the manipulation of abstractions (and in a different sense it has not been settled even in our own day). This was only one of the many issues on which Cartesian philosophy threatened to cause theological disputes, and Descartes himself was so upset and frightened by the news of Galileo's condemnation that he called off publication of his highly speculative work *Le Monde*: it finally appeared well after his death, in 1664. In all his cosmological works he took great pains, as a good Catholic, to emphasise that he offered only hypotheses, not certain truths, This was excessively cautious, since he spent the greatest part of his life in Protestant Holland, whose relatively tolerant atmosphere allowed him to pursue his studies uninterrupted.

All the saving clauses imaginable could not have made Descartes's mechanistic philosophy acceptable to the traditionalist scholars of the French universities, and it never achieved the status of an official doctrine. But in less backward-looking circles it quickly became the rage, and by the 1660s had arrived as the dominant feature of intellectual life in France and other European countries. The great scientists of the next generation, such as Leibniz and Huygens, were brought up on the Cartesian system, and their thought was profoundly marked by it. In England its influence was great, but the native tradition associated with Bacon remained strong, and helped prevent the establishment of a new orthodoxy. The grave inadequacies of the new system mattered less, in the short run at least, than the immense stimulus it gave to the efforts of other scientists to mathematise and analyse the natural world. Descartes was at once the last of the Schoolmen, presenting a qualitative sketch instead of an exact quantitative description, and the inspiration for the new generation of experimental scientists [**doc. 7**] (**20, 46, 47**).

THE CORPUSCULAREAN THEORISTS

It was not difficult to make a distinction between approval of Descartes's mechanical picture of the universe in general and acceptance of his detailed theories. While there was wide agreement that he had shown the way towards a new cosmology, one of the basic principles on which he had built was already under attack at the time of his death. This was his assertion of the logical impossibility of a void or vacuum in nature. Another French thinker, Pierre Gassendi (1592–1655), took up the atomic theory suggested by the ancient Greeks Democritus and Epicurus. In many ways Gassendi's atoms were no different from Descartes's particles, but they moved in a vacuum instead of having the gaps between them filled with 'subtle matter'. He produced several very respectable philosophical arguments for the possibility of such a vacuum, and these were gladly adopted by other scientists anxious to escape from the densely packed Cartesian world. But Gassendi was no more successful than Descartes in giving expression to the hypothetical motions of his atoms, and there was little reason to prefer his ideas, which were in general far less plausible (**49**).

Philosophical arguments for the existence of a vacuum became much more convincing when they were supported by one of the great experimental achievements of the period. This was the barometric experiment devised by Toricelli and known by his name, but perfected by the French philosopher and scientist Blaise Pascal (1623–62). When it was shown that a liquid in a tube, one of whose ends was sealed and the other immersed in the liquid in a wider vessel, could not remain suspended above a certain level, the nature of the resulting empty space had to be explained. In 1648 Pascal demonstrated that the height of the column of mercury (used because its high specific gravity allowed the apparatus to be kept reasonably small) varied with altitude, by having simultaneous measurements carried out at the top and the foot of a small mountain, the Puy-de-Dôme. He argued that the column was supported by the pressure of the air, which decreased as it became more rarefied with height, and that the empty space was indeed a vacuum.

Descartes was willing to accept the air pressure theory, but naturally denied the existence of a real vacuum, on the grounds that subtle matter would pass easily through the glass wall of the tube. This objection was logically irrefutable in terms of his system, but Pascal's explanation was far more convincing, and he emerged an easy victor from his controversies with supporters of Descartes. By carrying out a series of controlled experiments with apparatus of different sizes he established beyond reasonable doubt that the air possessed weight, and that this was the explanation of the regular height of the column.

Further experimental evidence for the existence of a vacuum was provided by the German Otto von Guericke, who devised an air pump which enabled him to evacuate any large airtight vessel. This device freed scientists from the restrictions of the very small empty spaces produced in the Toricellian tube, and was one of the most important technical inventions of the century. It gave a direct inspiration to the work of Robert Boyle (1627–91), the most important and influential of the 'corpusculareans'. Boyle, in collaboration with Robert Hooke, worked on problems of atmospheric pressure and the vacuum in the late 1650s. These experiments led him to the formulation of the law which is known by his name: he wrote 'that pressures and expansions be in reciprocal proportions'. In modern terminology, he connected the pressure and volume of a gas at a constant temperature ($pv = k$), with specific reference to air.

Boyle is often regarded as the father of modern chemistry, but his famous book *The Sceptical Chymist* (1661) does not really justify this claim. The cast of his mind was very cautious, as the title implied, and he showed his distrust of premature certainty in such statements as 'I met with very few opinions that I can certainly acquiesce in'. The chief achievement of the book was to attack the Aristotelian and Paracelsian theories about the nature of matter, by demonstrating that their supposed 'elements' could not actually be identified in any known experiment. But Boyle's own proposals for replacement elements were not very satisfactory, and chemistry in the modern sense was not to begin for more than a century, with the work of Lavoisier and Dalton.

Apart from many attempts at straightforward analysis, Boyle concerned himself with the preparation of dyes and medicines, and with alchemy. Once involved with this last, he showed most of the credulity typical of its practitioners, and the normal critical tone disappeared from his writings. He may well have been attracted less by the prospect of wealth—of which he already possessed a good deal—than by the hope of finding the universal remedy or elixir of life, belief in whose existence was still general.

Boyle's chemical interests were not merely important in themselves, but provided the groundwork for his own version of the mechanistic philosophy, first presented in detail in *The Origin of Forms and Qualities According to the Corpuscular Philosophy*, of 1666. Like Gassendi, he employed a modified version of the ancient atomic theories. The only principles of scientific explanation he would permit were those derived from matter, divided into particles, and motion. In effect he wished to prove that quantitative operations led to qualitative change, and he cited a large number of experiments to demonstrate that natural processes could be explained much better in this way than by Aristotelian doctrines of form. The quantitative operations he envisaged were those on the bulk, figure, motion and texture of the minuter parts of bodies, and the re-arrangements of these primary properties were his explanation for the qualitative changes experienced through the senses. This statement of the theoretical basis of the mechanical and corpuscularean philosophy was both clearer and less open to philosophical objections than anything which had preceded it. Boyle was also concerned to defend atomism against religious objections, and his efforts in this direction were successful enough in his day, partly because of his social standing as the son of an earl and his undoubted piety (**37, 49**).

The Dutch scientist Christiaan Huygens (1629–95) sought to apply the kind of method suggested by Boyle, although his original inspiration came from the work of Descartes. He rejected the use of 'qualities' and 'forms' in scientific explanation, and was another advocate of the 'motion and particles' approach. His Cartesianism did not extend to denial of the vacuum, and he also rejected the idea that matter could be divided into a mere three categories. Instead he supposed that the possible number of variations was virtually infinite, and that particles moved faster the smaller they were. This idea shackled him to the concept of vortices, and so he was unable to escape entirely from the tradition of Descartes in this respect. But he broke new ground with his theory of light, based on the passage of impulses through ether particles, and he improved greatly on the vortex theory of Descartes by making experiments on centrifugal force. He was able to give a mathematical description of its operation in terms of velocity, mass, and distance from the centre. This was an important contribution, but Huygens failed to exploit it properly, since he did not apply it to celestial motion. He was unable to reconstruct the motions of the planets properly in terms of his spherical vortices, and confined his investigations of gravity to terrestrial physics. In most ways Huygens was the most rigorously mechanistic of all seventeenth-century scientists, and his extreme application of the method was ultimately rather self-defeating and constricting (20).

THE SOCIETIES

The gradual emergence of an informal scientific community had been very much the affair of the scientists themselves. But as the educated section of European society was brought more and more into contact with the intellectual revolution taking place in its midst, interest became more general. Knowledge was partly spread by the numerous polemical and popularising books and tracts which were published, but more widely and surely by new medical techniques and instruments such as the telescope. The notion that the world was declining towards its end became less fashionable, and awareness of new scientific discoveries helped to accelerate the demise of this pessimistic concept. Princes and noblemen began to interest themselves in science as they had previously done in theology, and became seriously concerned to promote research into the secrets of nature once they were convinced it was possible to discover them.

In the early 1660s, which were notable for being the first years of general European peace since the outbreak of the Thirty Years War, important national institutions were founded in both London and Paris with royal support. They were very different: the English

Royal Society was a loose group of people either active or interested in science, while the French Académie des Sciences had a fixed number of members (16), who were effectively scientific researchers on state pensions. Scientific journals also appeared in both countries, the *Philosophical Transactions* associated with the Royal Society and the independent *Journal des Sçavans*, and had an obvious importance in stimulating scientific activity.

The Académie is of greater interest for the intentions of its founder Colbert than for any direct contribution it made to the scientific revolution. The French statesman was convinced that the application of new scientific knowledge to technological problems would make for industrial and agricultural progress, and therefore produce economic benefits. His imaginative programme for such an attempt was ruined by the renewal of warfare from 1672 onwards, which prevented the allocation of the necessary financial resources. Left very much to its own devices, the Académie showed most originality in biology, comparative anatomy and botany rather than the physical sciences. In the long run this was to prove an extremely rewarding decision, but the immediate results were disappointing, and certainly had little practical application.

The Royal Society experienced similar difficulties in distinguishing the genuinely important matters from the vast mass of trivia, which even its most distinguished members tended to introduce from time to time. Historians have often grossly overestimated the Society's importance, and regarded membership as proof of a degree of involvement with science certainly not possessed by the more dilettante aristocratic members. Even royal patronage of the Society did not make the new philosophy acceptable to the ultra-conservative universities of Oxford and Cambridge, although individual dons were favourably inclined, particularly in Cambridge. One of the Society's main contributions at first was to try and forge stronger links between the scientists and the world of affairs: a good deal of its time was spent in examining the possibilities of drawing practical benefit from scientific technology in a manner Colbert would have approved (**9, 51, 52, 53**).

Much of the most fruitful work done in connection with the Society during its early years was inspired by Robert Hooke (1635–1703), its Curator of Experiments and later its Secretary (**64**). A man of great energy and ingenuity, he was continually proposing new subjects for investigation, and devising the necessary experimental techniques. Hooke was interested in everything: microscopy, astronomy, geology, optics, and anything else that happened to cross his path. With this great facility went a certain inability to stick at any one subject for long enough, and a readiness to accept imperfect answers, which prevented him from making any single great contribution to science. But as a stimulus to Newton and Boyle, in particular, he was a major indirect inspiration for many of the discoveries of other men. This was ultimately very much the rôle of the societies as well: science had yet to reach the point at which really profitable schemes for group research could be instigated, and before this stage such institutions were chiefly of value for making communication between individual scientists easier, and encouraging the growth of a general public interest in science and technology. They also made their members much more conscious of the need to employ proper methods of research, and their influence helped to generalise the principles of the 'experimental philosophy'.

MEDICINE, BIOLOGY AND OTHER SCIENCES

Many of the early members of the Royal Society were doctors, and medicine was the branch of scientific activity which had the most immediate impact on the public. There were varied intellectual currents in the profession at this date, and the official Royal College of Physicians was unable to enforce obedience to its decrees in face of the widespread demand for more effective methods of treatment. The traditional Galenist school was confronted by the iatrochemists, who were advocates of chemical medicines on Paracelsian lines, and those who were in need of medical attention had the choice between these two, or often a combination of them, and the innumerable quacks offering their unique methods and certain cures. Whichever school they chose, it was probably largely a matter of luck whether or not they benefited from the treatment, which must often have been positively harmful. There was some slight improvement in standards over the century, with the introduction of new drugs such as quinine, a better understanding of others like mercury and opium, and a gradual tendency away from violent over dosing. A revolution in medical practice was still a long way off, but at least the need for it was coming to be widely realised, and discoveries about the physiology of men and animals were helping to bring it nearer [**doc. 8**] (**39, 41**).

The most striking of all these advances in medical knowledge was that made by the English physician William Harvey with his discovery of the circulation of the blood (1628). It is interesting to note that Harvey compared the heart to a mechanical pump, and supported his theory by calculations on the amount of blood the body would have to produce every day if there were no circulatory system. In this sense his work was linked with the new methods of the mechanical sciences, although he owed most to the work of his teachers at Padua (43). Unfortunately there were few immediate results of Harvey's achievement, which took a long time to win general approval, and it did not even seem to discourage the practice of bleeding patients at the slightest provocation.

Other physiologists were making a series of useful if less spectacular contributions throughout the century, working chiefly on the lymphatic system, the brain, and the internal organs. The invention of the microscope at the beginning of the century made it possible to study anatomy in unprecedented detail, and Hooke, Malpighi, Leuwenhoek and Swammerdam were the leading figures in this new branch of activity. Much of their work was on the anatomy of small creatures, such as the silkworms studied by Malpighi and the invertebrates of Swammerdam. But the microscope could also reveal the hidden structure of the human body, and Leuwenhoek was particularly active in this direction, discovering the red corpuscles in the blood, the capillary circulation, bacteria, spermatozoa, and a great deal besides. Although these achievements attracted widespread interest, and a good deal of incredulity, they were difficult to fit into any general system, and were not of immediate utility.

Much of the work done in zoology and botany was also of a preliminary kind, and suffered from the lack of satisfactory overall systems of classification. A mass of information about thousands of species and varieties was collected, but no one knew quite what to do with it or how to interpret it. These sciences still lacked a proper methodology, and in its absence did little more than arouse curiosity and make people aware of the vast range and complexity of the animal and vegetable worlds.

The information that there had been yet other creatures, now vanished, at an earlier stage of the earth's development, was a contribution of the new science of geology. Although the nature of fossils had been understood by some before him, such as Leonardo, Nicolaus Steno (1638–86) was the first to study them systematically, and to see the importance of the different layers in which they were found. Science was coming on to dangerous ground here, for the theory of geological periods based on advances and retreats of the oceans did not accord very well with the age of the world from the Creation, as calculated from the Bible. Not only did a mere 4,000 years or so, the accepted age of the earth, leave far too little time for all this to occur at a plausible rate, but the only description of such an event in the Bible was that of the Great Flood, which could hardly explain the different layers. But for a long time to come geologists were to be too pious, or too afraid, to challenge the theological position, and the final conflict would only arise with Darwin's theory of evolution in the nineteenth century.

It should not be thought that these other scientific activities were unimportant, just because they failed to come of age in the seventeenth century as physics and astronomy did. Even the collection of disorganised knowledge was useful, and the establishment of a tradition of scholarly enquiry in each discipline was a great step forward. As the century progressed it became clearer that the moderns had surpassed the ancients on every front, and could go further still. The substitution of a belief in progress towards greater knowledge for the late medieval conviction that the world was inexorably declining was of immense psychological value to the scientists. It was a belief to whose growth they themselves contributed enormously by demonstrating that it was possible to know more than the Greeks had done about all the ramifications of the natural world, and every branch of science had its part to play in this operation.

5 The Newtonian Synthesis

THE BACKGROUND TO THE *PRINCIPIA*

Despite the great advances in knowledge described so far, the new philosophy was still more convincing in detail than in general. The ingenious system of Descartes and its derivatives might be attractive to those who wished to replace Aristotle, but the example of Huygens shows how difficult it was to develop it into a precise mathematical description of reality. The Cartesian universe was choked with matter, and operated through physical contacts so frequent and so complex that they defied analysis. The search after physical reality had become a dangerous obsession, and threatened to establish a new kind of intellectual stranglehold on scientific thought. It was probably fortunate that the new theories were not successful in displacing Aristotelianism from the universities, and remained the subject of sharp controversy. In the resulting atmosphere of intellectual excitement and tension the imperfections of both ancients and moderns were exposed, and the need for further systematisation emphasised.

The genius of Isaac Newton (1642–1727) seems to have been stimulated by many of the great controversies of his age, and the scientific work for which he is famed was far from being his only concern. From his papers it would appear that over his lifetime he devoted almost as much attention to alchemy and chemistry as to the physical sciences, and that even more of his efforts went into theology and chronology. To these widespread interests Newton brought not only a brilliant mind, but also a very independent one; he worked alone, using the ideas of others to his own purposes without allowing them to dominate him. He moved unpredictably from one subject to another, sometimes taking up discontinued researches again years later, or leaving his intuitions for his successors to exploit and improve. This erratic behaviour may surprise those who think of Newton as the first 'modern' scientist, but it was typical of many thinkers of the seventeenth century. In many ways Newton resembled Hooke, his superiority being largely as a mathematician;

his abilities in this respect marked him off from all his English contemporaries.

From early in his Cambridge career, which began in 1661, Newton seems to have been acquainted with the work of his three great predecessors, Kepler, Galileo, and Descartes. He was both excited and provoked by the last of these, scrawling critical comments all over the margins of his *Geometry*, and in a sense his scientific career was to be a kind of dialogue with the Cartesian theories. Although in no way an exceptional student to begin with, by the end of three years he was the equal of the Professor of Mathematics, the great Isaac Barrow. At this point the university was closed because of the Great Plague, and Newton returned home to Lincolnshire. At this period he laid the foundations of his later triumphs: he worked out the basis of his theory of colours, and developed the mathematical technique of 'fluxions' which was his version of the infinitesimal calculus. Most important of all, as he himself described it many years later:

> I began to think of gravity extending to the orb of the Moon, and having found out how to estimate the force with which [a] globe revolving within a sphere passes the surface of the sphere, from Kepler's Rule of the periodical times of the Planets being in a sesquialterate proportion of their distances from the centres of their orbs I deduced the forces which keep the Planets in their Orbs must [be] reciprocally as the squares of their distances from the centres about which they revolve; and thereby compared the force requisite to keep the Moon in her Orb with the force of gravity at the surface of the earth, and found them answer pretty nearly. All this was in the two plague years of 1665 and 1666, for in those days I was in the prime of my age for invention, and minded Mathematics and Philosophy more than at any time since (**6**).

It would appear that although Newton found the answer 'pretty nearly', his measurements for the size of the earth in relation to the moon were very inadequate, and therefore the error was quite considerable. He may have been disappointed by this, and when he returned to Cambridge in 1667 became absorbed in mathematics, optics and alchemy.

Newton succeeded Barrow as Professor in 1669, and became a Fellow of the Royal Society in 1671 on the strength of the reflecting telescope he had developed. This brought him into closer contact with Hooke, who had also been making intermittent stabs at the problem of explaining planetary motion. In a public experiment at a meeting of the Society in 1666 Hooke had demonstrated how it was possible to make a pendulum move in an ellipse by exerting a constant pull towards the centre with a wire fixed to the bob weight. He also constructed a more complicated model to represent the moon's motion around the earth, which showed how the earth's own orbit around the sun was affected. In 1670 Hooke lectured to the Royal Society and laid down the principles of a new cosmology:

I shall . . . hereafter explain a system of the world differing in many particulars from any yet known, but answering in all things to the common rule of mechanical motions. This depends on three suppositions: *first*, That all celestial bodies whatsoever have an attraction or gravitating power towards their own centres, whereby they attract not only their own parts, and keep them from flying from them, as we may observe the Earth to do, but they also do attract all the other celestial bodies that are within the sphere of their activity, and consequently that not only the Sun and Moon have an influence on the body and motion of the Earth, and the Earth upon them, but that Mercury, Venus, Mars, Jupiter, and Saturn also, by their attractive powers, have a considerable influence upon its motion, as in the same manner the corresponding attractive power of the Earth hath a considerable influence upon every one of their motions also, The *second* supposition is this, that all bodies whatsoever that are put into a direct and simple motion, will so continue to move forward in a straight line until they are, by some other effectual powers, deflected, and sent into motion describing a circle, ellipsis, or some more compounded curve line. The *third* supposition is, that these attractive powers are so much the more powerful in operating by how much nearer the body wrought upon is to their own centres. Now, what these several degrees are, I have not yet experimentally verified, but it is a notion which, if fully presented, as it ought to be, will mightily assist the astronomers to reduce all the celestial motion to a certain rule, which I doubt will never be done without it.

This passage is a brilliant anticipation of Newton's theory of universal gravitation, but it does not make Hooke the discoverer of the laws of gravitation. He did not succeed in his attempts to verify the theory experimentally, since he lacked the necessary mathematical skill, and also failed to correct an important error by Kepler.

73

It is essential to realise that by this stage in the development of science intuitions were not enough, and had to be backed up by properly constructed arguments.

Newton's original contacts with the Royal Society had led to a bitter quarrel between him and Hooke over their respective theories of light and colours, partly disagreement over accuracy and partly over priority of discovery. After 1676 Newton effectively withdrew from participation in the Society, and in 1677 Hooke became its Secretary. It was in this capacity that he addressed a letter to Newton at the end of 1679, inviting him to resume his relations with the Society, and asking his opinions on several scientific topics of the moment. He also sought comments on his own theories:

> For my part I shall take it as a great favour if you shall please communicate by letter your objections against any hypothesis or opinion of mine; and particularly if you will let me know your thoughts of that of compounding the celestiall motions of the planetts of a direct motion by the tangent and an attractive motion towards the centrall body, or what objections you have against my hypothesis of the lawes or causes of springynesse.

Newton wrote back a politely crushing letter, making it clear that he was not enthusiastic, but suggesting an experiment on the trajectory of a heavy body, falling to the earth or towards its centre. In doing so he made an error concerning the shape of the curve it would describe, and Hooke pointed this out, starting a further argument between the two men, in which both were at fault—and neither could give an adequate answer to the problem. By January 1680 Newton had stopped answering Hooke's letters, but his interest had been drawn back to questions he had apparently hardly touched for many years.

It seems that during the period of his correspondence with Hooke in 1679–80 Newton solved the problem of Kepler-motion, by making a direct mathematical relation between Kepler's first two laws. Using the third law, he was able to prove that the planets travelled in ellipses under the constant action of a force, and that force was entirely directed towards the sun, varying inversely with the square of the distance. Having performed this feat, he appears to have lost interest again, and it is difficult to understand why. He may have been unable to make his tests of the law of gravitation work properly, because of his earlier mistakes about the moon. Alternatively, he may have been troubled by inability to prove that a gravitating sphere can be treated as if all its mass were at the centre, a hurdle he did not overcome until 1685. Whatever the reason, he did not proceed, and told no one of his work. But in 1684 the famous astronomer Halley called on Newton at Cambridge and asked his help; he had appreciated that Kepler's Third Law amounted to an inverse-square law, but was unable to work out the planetary orbits that would result. In a famous conversation Newton told him that he had already proved that the orbit would be an ellipse. But it turned out that with true professorly absent-mindedness he had mislaid the proof, and he had to promise that he would send it on later. This final stimulus led to the writing of the *Mathematical Principles of Natural Philosophy*, the first book of which was laid before the Royal Society in 1686. At last Newton had carried through the intuitions of his youth, and turned them into a systematic account of the framework of the universe. With the publication of this great work in 1687 a new era in the history of science began, although it would take half a century for this to be universally acknowledged [**doc. 9**] (**46, 47, 48, 49, 64**).

THE NATURE OF THE NEWTONIAN SYSTEM

The very title of his great work betrayed something of Newton's intentions. Where Descartes had laid down the Principles of Philosophy, he would lay down the *Mathematical* principles. This was at once an advance and a self-imposed limitation, for while the mathematical description of nature could be tested by experiment, and examined for internal self-consistency, it did not constitute a complete description of the world in qualitative terms. In retrospect we can see that it was essential for science to free itself from the need to explain everything, and to restore a certain freedom of action by the introduction of identifiable but inexplicable elements into the world picture. But it was less easy for contemporaries: Newton himself was always dissatisfied with his inability to explain gravity and forces, and it was the great objection of Huygens, Leibniz and other continental thinkers that he had brought 'occult qualities' back into philosophy.

Newton did not reject the ideas of his immediate predecessors, and employed the same basic set of concepts, although he was more careful than most to give the 'axiomatic' definitions. Atoms, mass, extension, figure or shape: these were the materials with which he worked. Motion was the rearrangement of atoms in space during time, and could involve two kinds of interaction. One of these was that envisaged by Descartes, the impact of one atom or collection of atoms on another, governed by the laws of momentum and elasticity. The other was the revolutionary innovation: gravity, or the action of atoms upon one another at a distance.

Newton could not explain attraction at a distance, but he was able to describe it mathematically by his inverse square law. In this way he combined the mathematical, Platonic vision of Galileo with the mechanical literalism of the Corpuscruleans. Both kinds of interaction were brought together in the concept of force, which completed the link between terrestrial and celestial dynamics. The Newtonian universe was made up of matter in motion in the void of absolute space, and the planets were subject to the same laws as cannon-balls. Newton was able to demonstrate that Descartes's arguments against the vacuum were philosophically inconsistent, and they were also incompatible with the observed behaviour of the heavenly bodies.

> Against filling the heavens with fluid mediums, unless they be exceeding rare, a great objection arises from the regular and very lasting motion of the planets and comets in all manner of courses through the heavens. For thence it is manifest that the heavens are void of all sensible resistance, and by consequnce of all sensible matter . . . [A Cartesian fluid] can be of no use for explaining the phenomena of nature: the motion of the planets and comets being better explained without it. It serves only to disturb and retard the motions of those great bodies, and make the Frame of Nature languish. . . . And as it is of no use . . . so there is no evidence for its existence and therefore it ought to be rejected (**6**).

The *Principia* was not an easy book to grasp as a whole, partly because its mathematical techniques were cumbersome; although Newton had developed his own version of the calculus, he stuck to the methods of Euclid and Apollonios for his proofs. But it did lay down a basic scheme for physics which neither Galileo nor any other previous thinker had equalled for clarity, brevity, and accuracy. Three simple Laws of Motion were stated at the outset:

1. Every body continues in its state of rest or of uniform rectilinear motion unless compelled to change its state by the action of forces.

2. The change of motion is proportional to the force acting, and takes place along the straight line along which the force acts.
3. There is always a reaction equal and opposite to action; or, the actions of two bodies on each other are always equal and opposite (**6**).

Everything which occurred in the world must be the result of the motion of some of its component parts, and therefore these laws were of universal application. But such motion would usually be the product of force, and so a series of laws concerning the operation of forces was also required. Newton had discovered one of these in his inverse-square law of gravitation, and most of the *Principia* was devoted to working out the consequences. The solar system was truly a vast mechanism, whose behaviour could be predicted to an astonishing degree; the planets were held in their complex paths by the counterbalancing forces of their tangential velocity and the gravitational attraction of the sun. Comets were a special case of the same phenomenon, with enormously prolonged elliptical orbits. The complications introduced by the subsidiary attractions between planets were to take many years to work out even approximately, but the new system had no difficulty in coping with them theoretically: it was a question of detailed observation and calculation.

There was no basic difference between this celestial machinery and Galilean terrestrial physics: the behaviour of moving bodies on earth was subject to the same laws of motion, but also to the resistance of the air and other media, and to the local gravitational field of the earth. The dreams of Pythagoreans and Platonists had been realised at last, and the world was shown to be organised according to a harmonious mathematical law. Well might the eminent French physicist Lagrange complain, a century later, that as there was only one universe to be explained, no one could repeat the act of Newton, the luckiest of mortals.

Newton lived on for another forty years after the publication of his masterpiece, but he did little more original work. He became a domineering President of the Royal Society, and occupied himself with problems of chronology and his duties as Master of the Royal Mint. Successive editions of the *Principia* were corrected and improved upon by his pupils under his control, and gradually the new orthodoxy came to be accepted on the Continent as well as in England.

Newton's other chief work, the *Opticks*, was held back until 1704 because he would not permit publication until after Hooke's death in consequence of another bitter quarrel between the two men. As might have been expected, it was a brilliant contribution to the study of light, colours and related subjects, but it cannot bear comparison with the *Principia* as a breakthrough to a new level of understanding. Much of its interest is as an example of Newton applying his own method to other subjects, with a mixture of success and failure as a result. But it was the speculative ideas of the *Opticks* rather than the mathematical rigour of the *Principia* which had the greatest influence on Newton's English disciples. It almost seemed as if the scale of his achievement had overawed them, and they preferred to develop the qualitative atomist side of his thought instead of tackling the difficult theoretical problems raised by the new mathematical physics. Only in the second half of the eighteenth century did continental astronomers and physicists, applying the Leibnizian calculus to these problems, carry forward the work of Newton, completing and correcting his system.

While the original opposition of men like Huygens and Leibniz had been based on the impossibility of action at a distance, unless it could be explained by mechanical means, this idea was later to be taken almost for granted. Scientists would come to speak of forces as if they were a sufficient explanation in themselves for natural phenomena. In this they were certainly going beyond anything Newton himself would have regarded as reasonable. His famous statement '*hypotheses non fingo*', correctly translated as 'I do not feign hypotheses', was not the positivist declaration for which it has often been mistaken. Once more Descartes was the target, for he had produced fantastic and *untestable* ideas, then assumed them to be true and used them as the building blocks of his philosophy. But Newton saw no harm in hypotheses, if they were kept in their place, and he did not think he had found the final answer. The mathematical identification of forces allowed one to be certain that they existed, but it was no more than an intermediate step. The first aim of science, as described at the end of the *Opticks*, was profoundly religious:

> The main business of natural philosophy is to argue from phenomena without feigning hypotheses, and to deduce causes from effects, till we come to the very first Cause, which certainly is not mechanical: and not only to unfold the mechanism of the world, but chiefly to resolve these and such like questions. What is there in places almost empty of matter, and whence is it that the sun

and planets gravitate towards one another, without dense matter between them? Whence is it that Nature doth nothing in vain; and whence arises all that order and beauty which we see in the world? To what end are comets, and whence is it that planets move all one and the same way in orbs concentric, while comets move all manner of ways in orbs very excentric; and what hinders the fixed stars from falling upon one another? How came the bodies of animals to be contrived with so much art, and for what ends were their several parts? Was the eye contrived without skill in optics, and the ear without knowledge of sounds? How do the motions of the body follow from the will, and whence is the instinct in animals? . . . And these things being rightly dispatched, does it not appear from phenomena that there is a Being incorporeal, living, intelligent, omnipresent, who in infinite space, as it were in His sensory, sees the things themselves intimately, and thoroughly perceives them, and comprehends them wholly by their immediate presence to Himself: of which things the images only carried through the organs of sense into our little sensoriums, are seen and beheld by that which in us perceives and thinks. And though every true step made in this philosophy brings us not immediately to the knowledge of the First Cause, yet it brings us nearer to it, and on that account is to be highly valued (**7**).

These are hardly the words of a cold-blooded empiricist, nor of one who considered God an irrelevance in a world ruled by impersonal mathematical laws. Like most innovators, Newton himself did not fully appreciate the extent of his achievement, and would have been profoundly shocked by many of its long-term consequences.

Part Three

CONCLUSIONS

6 Why was there a Scientific Revolution?

This question would probably be unanswerable, even if we possessed all the evidence for which one could possibly ask. The historian can only hope to identify the most important causal factors, and then rank them in a rough order of importance on largely subjective grounds.

Only at a certain level of general culture is a scientific revolution possible at all; Neanderthal men, the Anglo-Saxons, the American Indians, and many other past cultures, ruled themselves out before they could even begin. They communicated by oral, not literary means, and therefore could not isolate the problems adequately nor develop theories of sufficient complexity about them. The Greeks and the early modern scientists lived in civilisations where literacy was on the increase, and were therefore particularly conscious of its potentialities. These societies were also undergoing other changes: they were evolving towards individualism at the expense of communal coherence, and towards intellectual speculation in the place of shared mythical certainties. The influences of printing, of economic advance and the development of a more fluid set of social distinctions, were obviously of vital importance in setting the scene for the revolution. We can see a general pattern below the surface chaos of events: the intellectual and organisational legacy of Greece was never entirely lost, and its progressive re-emergence during the Middle Ages was the trigger for a new wave of activity. The pressure exerted by population growth on resources and on the systems of political control militated against a static world order, however much contemporaries hankered after its security.

But although this social and cultural background was a fundamental prerequisite for the revolution, it was not a sufficient cause in itself. Very similar conditions in China led to an elaborate but conservative culture, which rapidly lost its original impetus. Chinese technology was highly advanced within certain limits, and yet it failed to stimulate the kind of theoretical debate which took

83

place in the West, although the latter was in many ways less 'civilised' during our period.

Attempts to explain the revolution in terms of the demands and stimulus of technology, itself interpreted as a function of social needs, have never been very convincing either. Again, a certain degree of technological advance was a necessary precondition, but it was not enough in itself to provoke the kind of fundamental crisis which would lead to a new conception of the structure of the world. And even such a crisis need not have been a specifically progressive force. The reaction of sixteenth-century sceptics or 'Pyrrhonists' like Erasmus or Montaigne to the problems of their time was essentially unconstructive, tending eventually to a renewed conformity based on universal doubt: if nothing could be certainly known, then why not accept existing compromises instead of fashioning inconvenient and dangerous new ones?

Similar objections apply to the suggested connection between Protestantism (or Puritanism) and science, for the conservatism of the Counter-Reformation Catholic church was often matched by Protestant biblical fundamentalism. It is probably true that men of radical political outlook were particularly sympathetic to the challenging side of the new science, but autocratic rulers were more effective in giving practical support after about 1660. The most that can safely be said is that the breakdown of the old order in both political and intellectual life was unquestionably of service to the scientists, and freed them of social and cultural restraints which had effectively inhibited their predecessors. Although by the sixteenth century the time was ripe for a scientific revolution, it remained for the scientists themselves to find an internal source of intellectual dynamism before it could actually take place (**67–75**).

In the end such an overthrow of long-established beliefs and structures of thought can probably only have come from the evolution of trends already present within the old system. It has been one of the chief objects of this book to show how from the Ancient World onwards the accepted neo-Aristotelian world view contained basic inconsistencies and points of dispute. Two of these in particular were to be of vital importance: the motion of projectiles and astronomy. The scholastic discussions of these topics led directly into the work of the later scientists we have been studying, and even the *Principia* is full of terms and definitions which had hardly altered over several centuries. The development of mathematics and its increasing rôle in the physical sciences was also a slow process, in which there were few dramatic discoveries, but rather a series of cumulative advances. In any case, the problem was far more one of applying even simple mathematics to physics than one of mathematics lagging behind the demands upon it. We have seen how technical difficulties in astronomy occupied all the major figures of the revolution: Copernicus, Kepler, Galileo, Descartes and Newton. There were only inadequate practical motives for their interest: chronology and astrology. The chief drive must surely have come from a desire to understand the universe, the product at once of intellectual curiosity and psychological insecurity.

For most natural philosophers of the sixteenth and seventeenth centuries the way seemed to lie through some great central set of harmonies or sympathies which held the universe together, but this usually meant systems we would call magical rather than scientific. Only the select few saw the need to measure and mathematise, and when Newton applied these techniques to physics and astronomy alike, the new key to the universe was revealed. But when the door was open and the secret exposed, it was a disappointment for many. Understanding might have been achieved, but it had not brought control with it, and a long road lay ahead. When Bacon said 'knowledge is power' he epitomised an illusory view of research in the pure sciences which has lasted in some quarters down to our own day.

Yet the illusion has been of great service, for it has encouraged patrons and scientists alike to pursue goals of which they might otherwise have despaired. This was one important function of the Platonism of the Renaissance, with its picture of an animistic world, tied together by a network of sympathies and occult influences which could be affected by human intervention. It inspired natural magicians, astrologers, alchemists and scientists alike (and indeed all these descriptions could often be applied to one man) with the hope that they might gain mastery over at least parts of the world machine. Few of them would have been satisfied with the dry theorems of Newton, when they had aimed at the universal remedy, the universal language, the power to predict the future, and so much else. However, even if Platonism with its associated doctrines encouraged such flights of fancy, it also provided an essential competitor to the Aristotelian tradition, and contributed enormously to that state of intellectual tension from which the New Philosophy emerged.

85

Conclusions

The general picture which finally appears is that of an intellectual revolution, with its own inner dynamism, taking place in the context of a favourable social, political, cultural and technological environment. Each of the elements involved had its own vital part to play, and without any of them the course of events might have been very different. But all we can be sure of is that these factors were interdependent, and that they combined to produce the greatest upheaval in the history of science.

7 The Consequences of the Scientific Revolution

In terms of science itself the results of the seventeenth-century break-through are obvious enough. The methods of classical science lead into modern science far more naturally than they had emerged from ancient and medieval thought, and the validity of Newton's system as a first approximation has not been destroyed by relativity or quantum mechanics. The New Philosophy had abandoned the investigation of the ultimate and true nature of things to study their behaviour as interdependent parts of a whole. This 'functional' attitude towards natural phenomena found its expression in the use of mathematical formulae to represent the relations between them, and remains a central principle of modern science. But it was not immediately appreciated by Newton's contemporaries; as has already been stressed, his English followers were really more interested in mechanical than in mathematical explanations, and did little to follow up his achievement. This was understandable, for the whole of seventeenth-century physical science was brought to fruition in the *Principia*, and no one, including Newton himself, had any clear idea of where to look for the pay-off. Only some fifty years later, as the dust of the controversies with Leibniz, Huygens, and the Cartesians began to settle, was Newtonian science taken up by a new generation: Maupertuis, Clairaut, D'Alembert, Euler, Lagrange, Laplace and others set out to perfect it. They had largely accomplished this task by the end of the eighteenth century in mechanics and astronomy, producing a system which seemed entirely self-consistent, and was not to be challenged until the beginning of our own century.

Of the other sciences, the one most immediately influenced by Newtonianism was chemistry. Newton's own chemical theories were not very satisfactory, but the application of his methods by Lavoisier and Priestley enabled them to lay the foundations of modern chemical analysis. By the end of the eighteenth century the way was prepared for Dalton's atomic theory of chemistry, perhaps the most completely successful of all the direct descendants of Newtonianism.

Conclusions

The experimental method naturally had its own contribution to make, both here and in the other sciences, but the basic aim was constant: to reduce the phenomena to a set of verifiable laws. Up to the sixteenth century the available models had been misleading and inadequate, and impatient attempts to employ them to impose some kind of order on sense data had generally been disastrous. But the search for an intellectual harmony underlying the surface disorder of the universe could hardly be carried out by any other method, and one of the great merits of the new science was that it could be profitably exploited in this way. Progress made in the fields of biology, heat, sound, magnetism, electricity and optics all bears witness to this fertility.

Models can be restrictive as well as stimulating, of course, and one must be careful not to assume that analogies with physics always had good results. Given the relatively primitive state of these other sciences, however, there can be no doubt that the gains far outweighed any possible losses. Above all, the final destruction of Aristotelianism freed scientists of every kind from the need to conform to an outdated and intellectually cramping system of beliefs.

It was not only in the other sciences that the results of this liberation were slow to show themselves. Despite the efforts of the societies, the anticipated cross-fertilisation with technology proved extremely difficult to bring about. The great inventions of the eighteenth century, such as the steam engine, new forms of industrial machinery, and new agricultural implements, owed little to theoretical science. Only when a certain degree of industrialisation had taken place, and more sophisticated techniques were required, did the chemists, metallurgists and engineers really come into their own. In the nineteenth century science would co-operate with capitalism and the new forms of industrial organisation to change the face of the world. There was no absolute reason why this should not have happened earlier: the knowledge existed, but it was not easy to persuade the possessors of capital that they could increase their profits by employing it. In a small-scale economy which provided ample cheap labour, the incentives for experimentation of this kind were low, and attitudes only really changed with the growth of a competitive market. Once there was a real demand for the application of theoretical knowledge to practical problems advance was rapid, and by the mid-nineteenth century something like the modern relationship between pure and applied science had been established.

The medical revolution brought about by the widespread introduction of chemicals and drugs during the nineteenth century was of enormous significance. Together with the increased agricultural productivity rendered possible by mechanisation and the controlled development of new strains of plants and animals, it has allowed the population of the globe to treble between 1850 and the present day. This tremendous increase may now seem to threaten mankind with appalling difficulties, both practical and ethical, but up to the present it has acted as a relentless stimulus to economic and technological advance. So we can see that the whole history of the world was changed by the scientific revolution, which has exerted a dominant influence on the recent development of mankind.

Whatever its long-term consequences, the new orthodoxy was part of a belief in progress and the power of human reason which reached its highest point in the eighteenth century—the Age of Reason. While this optimistic spirit had been increasingly in evidence during the middle and later years of the seventeenth century, it was the triumph of the new science which finally confirmed its supremacy. Both the confusion and the excitement of the Renaissance were replaced by a mood of materialistic self-assurance. Despite Newton's own piety, his system allowed God to be reduced to the rôle of a divine clockmaker, who had only to set the machine in motion and then retire to contemplate the results. The orderly pattern of the universe seemed to demonstrate the benevolence and wisdom of God rather than his terrors, and encouraged a vague and undemanding Deism, if not outright disbelief.

The eighteenth century was the last—perhaps the only—age in which there was a widely held belief in human perfectibility, based on an essentially mechanistic conception not only of the universe, but of men's bodies and souls. In philosophy the dominant attitude was based on analysis into atomic constituents, and Hume described his theory of the association of ideas as 'a kind of attraction, which in the mental world will be found to have as extraordinary effects as in the natural, and to show itself in as many and as various forms'. The object of philosophers like Locke, Hume and Condorcet was to achieve a science of mind which would parallel that of nature, and to formulate a set of laws which would account for the behaviour of men. Once such laws were discovered, they thought it would be possible to discover what men really wanted, and to create a society which would give it to them. Behind this confidence lay a conception of truth as an absolute and harmonious body of knowledge, which it lay within the power of man to reveal. The reasons for the later breakdown of this rationalist faith are complex, but among them was certainly the error in which the eighteenth-century philosophers had followed the Greek intellectuals: their disregard for the passions, the irrational forces in the human personality. The French Revolution and the Romantic movement were to mark the end of the Age of Reason, and the beginning of a new era of doubt and confusion in human affairs.

Newton and his followers might have given the *coup de grâce* to Aristotle, but they had not fully replaced him. Supplying a model for the other sciences was not the same thing as formulating a set of natural 'qualities' whose interplay explained all known phenomena. The analytical power and precision of the new science was unprecedented, but it was paid for in a certain narrowing of range. This was the beginning of a process which has continued until our own day: the pursuit of the particular and testable aspects of nature to the increasing exclusion of the general.

This tendency towards specialisation has increased not only our positive knowledge, but also our awareness of our ignorance. Present-day physicists and mathematicians are conscious that they *cannot* know everything, for there are limits both to measurement and to logic itself. In this way science has eventually fragmented our world and diminished communal certainties. On the one hand it has given man an extraordinary degree of control over his environment. On the other it has contributed powerfully towards the growth of an intellectual and moral relativism which has complicated the task of exploiting this potential to positive ends. While the influence of the Newtonian model remains strong in the social sciences—linguistics, economics, psychology, sociology, anthropology—it has proved singularly difficult to produce anything like sets of laws in these fields. It seems at least arguable that it has outgrown its usefulness here, and has come to have the same kind of restrictive effect as was once exercised by Aristotelianism.

Our modern dilemmas can, almost without exception, be traced back to the great intellectual revolution which reached a climax in the seventeenth century. Men's attitudes towards their own nature and that of the world, towards God, politics and morals, have been fundamentally influenced and changed in consequence. If the object of history is to aid us to understand ourselves, the wars and treaties of this period are insignificant in comparison with the achievement of a handful of scientific researchers. They cannot be blamed if their successors have proved incapable of a social and psychological maturity which would ensure that man's new technological mastery was turned to good rather than evil ends. In this respect the failure of the eighteenth-century philosophers to develop a satisfactory science of mind was crucial, and has yet to be remedied. But however dubious the use mankind has made of its fruits, the scientific revolution will always remain a pre-eminent example of the triumph of mind over matter, and of intelligence over confusion.

D

Part Four

DOCUMENTS

ARISTOTLE: THE GREAT AUTHORITY

In this passage from his Physics *Aristotle attempts to solve the problem of projectile motion, which it was virtually impossible to fit into his system. His explanation convinced few serious thinkers, and was to be a prime target for his critics.*

If everything that is in motion is being moved by something, how comes it that certain things, missiles for example, that are not self-moving nevertheless continue their motion without a break when no longer in contact with the agent that gave them motion? Even if that agent at the same time that he puts the missile in motion also sets something else (say air) in motion, which something when itself in motion has power to move other things, still when the prime agent has ceased to be in contact with this secondary agent and has therefore ceased to be moving it, it must be just as impossible for it as for the missile to be in motion the instant the prime mover ceases to move them; and this holds good even if the prime agent is like the magnet, which has power to confer upon the iron bar it moves the power of moving another iron bar. We are forced, therefore, to suppose that the prime mover conveys to the air (or water, or other such intermediary as is naturally capable both of moving and conveying motion) a power of conveying motion, but that this power is not exhausted when the intermediary ceases to be moved itself. Thus the intermediary will cease to be moved itself as soon as the prime mover ceases to move it, but will still be able to move something else. Thus this something else will be put in motion after the prime mover's action has ceased, and will itself continue the series. The end of it all will approach as the motive power conveyed to each successive secondary agent wanes, till at last there comes one which can only move its neighbour without being able to convey motive force to it. At this point the last active intermediary will cease to convey motion, the passive intermediary that has no active power will cease to be in motion, and the missile will come to a stand, at the same instant. Now this movement occurs in things that are sometimes in motion and sometimes stationary, and it is not continuous, although it appears to be. For there is a succession of contiguous agents, since there is no one motor concerned but a series, one following upon another.

Physics, VIII. x, translated by P. H. Wicksteed and F. M. Cornford.

DIACETTO: THE RENAISSANCE MAGUS

A disciple of Ficino, Diacetto was much more explicit than his master in his description of the rites employed in 'natural magic'. He gave a programme for 'the diligent capturer of planetary light', which demonstrates the almost childlike symbolism involved.

If for example he wishes to acquire solarian gifts, first he sees that the Sun is ascending in Leo or Aries, on the day and in the hour of the Sun. Then, robed in a solarian mantle of a solarian colour, such as gold, and crowned with a wreath of laurel, on the altar, itself made of solarian material, he burns myrrh and frankincense, the Sun's own fumigations, having strewn the ground with heliotrope and such flowers. Also he has an image of the Sun in gold or chrysolite or carbuncle, that is, of the kind they think corresponds to each of the Sun's gifts. If, for example, he wishes to cure diseases, he has an image of the Sun enthroned, crowned, and wearing a saffron cloak, likewise a raven and the figure of the Sun, which are to be engraved on gold when the Sun is ascending in the first face of Leo. Then, anointed with unguents made, under the same celestial aspect, from saffron, balsam, yellow honey and anything else of that kind, and not forgetting the cock and the goat, he sings the Sun's own hymn, such as Orpheus thought should be sung. For here is the force, and as it were the life, of the conciliation of the planet's favour. He sings, I say, firstly to the divine Henad of the Sun, then he sings to the Mind, and lastly he sings to the soul, since One, Mind, Soul are the three principles of all things. Also he uses a threefold harmony, of voice, of cithern, and of the whole body, of the kind he has discovered belongs to the Sun; not one which by too much complexity produces wantonness, or which constantly displays gravity, but one which is the mean between these two, which both is joyful by its simplicity, and at times does not avoid a mood of gravity. To all these he adds what he believes to be the most important: a strongly emotional disposition of the imagination, by which, as with pregnant women, the spirit is stamped with this kind of imprint, and flying out through the channels of the body, especially through the eyes, ferments and solidifies, like rennet, the kindred power of the heavens.

From *Demonic and Spiritual Magic from Ficino to Campanella* (**60**).

document 3

COPERNICUS: THE OBSESSION WITH CIRCULARITY

In these two chapters from the first book of De Revolutionibus *Copernicus gives an exemplary Aristotelian defence of circular motion as the only possibility for the heavenly bodies, and then extends this reasoning to the earth. He is a traditionalist even when making a revolutionary proposal.*

4. That the Motion of the Heavenly Bodies is Uniform, Circular, and Perpetual, or composed of Circular Motions.

We now note that the motion of heavenly bodies is circular. Rotation is natural to a sphere and by that very act is its shape expressed. For here we deal with the simplest kind of body, wherein neither beginning nor end may be discerned nor, if it rotate ever in the same place, may the one be distinguished from the other.

Because there are a multitude of spheres, many motions occur. Most evident to sense is the diurnal rotation . . . marking day and night. By this motion the whole Universe, save Earth alone, is thought to glide from East to West. This is the common measure of all motions, since Time itself is numbered in days. Next we see other revolutions in contest, as it were, with this daily motion and opposing it from West to East. Such opposing motions are those of Sun and Moon and the five planets. . . .

But these bodies exhibit various differences in their motion. First their axes are not that of the diurnal rotation, but of the Zodiac, which is oblique thereto. Secondly, they do not move uniformly even in their own orbits; for are not Sun and Moon found now slower, now swifter in their courses? Further, at times the five planets become stationary at one point and another, and even go backward. . . . Furthermore, sometimes they approach the Earth, being then in *Perigee*, while at other times receding they are in *Apogee*.

Nevertheless, despite these irregularities, we must conclude that the motions of these bodies are ever circular or compounded of circles. For the irregularities themselves are subject to a definite law and recur at stated times, and this could not happen if the motions were not circular, for a circle alone thus can restore the place of a body as it was. So with the Sun, which, by a compounding of circular motions, brings ever again the changing days and nights and the four seasons of the year. Now therein it must be that divers motions are conjoined, since a simple celestial body cannot move irregularly in a single circle. For such irregularity must come of unevenness either in the moving force (whether inherent or acquired) or in the form of the revolving body. Both these alike the mind abhors regarding the most perfectly disposed bodies.

It is then generally agreed that the motions of Sun, Moon and Planets do but seem irregular either by reason of the divers directions of their axes of revolution, or else by reason that Earth is not the centre of the circles in which they revolve, so that to us on Earth the displacements of these bodies seem greater when they are near than when they are more remote (as is demonstrated in optics). Thus, equal motions of a sphere, viewed from different distances, will seem to cover different distances in equal times. It is therefore above all needful to observe carefully the relation of the Earth toward the Heavens, lest, searching out the things on high, we should pass by those nearer at hand, and mistakenly ascribe earthly qualities to heavenly bodies.

5. Whether Circular Motion belongs to the Earth; and concerning its position.

Since it has been shown that the Earth is spherical, we now consider whether her motion is conformable to her shape and her position in the Universe. Without these we cannot construct a proper theory of the heavenly phenomena. Now authorites agree that Earth holds firm her place at the centre of the Universe, and they regard the contrary as unthinkable, nay as absurd. Yet if we examine more closely it will be seen that this question is not so settled, and needs wider consideration.

A seeming change of place may come of movement either of object or observer, or again of unequal movement of the two (for between equal and parallel motions no movement is perceptible). Now it is Earth from which the rotation of the Heavens is seen. If then some motion of Earth be assumed it will be reproduced in external bodies, which will seem to move in the opposite direction.

Consider first the diurnal rotation. By it the whole Universe, save Earth alone and its contents, appears to move very swiftly. Yet grant that Earth revolves from West to East, and you will find, if you ponder it, that my conclusion is right. It is the vault of Heaven that contains all things, and why should not motion be attributed rather to the contained than to the container, to the located than the locator? The latter view was certainly that of Heraclides and Ecphantus the Pythagorean and Hicetas of Syracuse (according to Cicero). All of them made the Earth rotate in the midst of the Universe, believing that the Stars set owing to the Earth coming in the way, and rise again when it has passed on.

If this is admitted, then a problem no less grave arises about the Earth's position, even though almost everyone has hitherto held that the earth is at the centre of the Universe. For grant that the Earth is not at the exact centre but at a distance from it which, while small compared to the starry sphere, is yet considerable compared with the spheres of the Sun and the other planets. Then calculate the consequent variations in their seeming motions, assuming these to be really uniform and about some centre other than the Earth's. One may then perhaps adduce a reasonable cause for the irregularity of these veritable motions. And indeed since the Planets are seen at varying distances from the Earth, the centre of Earth is surely not the centre of their circles. Nor is it certain whether the Planets move toward and away from Earth, or Earth toward and away from them. It is therefore justifiable to hold that the Earth has another motion in addition to the diurnal rotation. That the Earth, besides rotating, wanders with several motions and is indeed a

Planet, is a view attributed to Philolaus the Pythagorean, no mean mathematician, and one whom Plato is said to have sought out in Italy.

From *Occasional Notes of the Royal Astronomical Society*, vol. ii, no. 10, trans. by J. F. Dobson and S. Brodetsky.

document 4

KEPLER: THE HEIR OF COPERNICUS AND BRAHE

In this extract from Harmonice Mundi *Kepler demonstrates how thoroughly he had absorbed the work of his great predecessors, and gives an admirable summary of the Tychonic system. There are also some characteristic mystical passages.*

Chief Points of Astronomical Learning, Necessary for the Contemplation of the Celestial Harmonies.

In the beginning let my readers understand this: that the old astronomical hypotheses of Ptolemy, as they are set forth in the Theoriae of Puerbach and the writings of the other epitomisers, are to be kept far from the present enquiry and banished wholly from the mind; for they fail to give a true account either of the arrangement of the heavenly bodies or of the laws governing their motions.

In their place I cannot do otherwise than substitute simply Copernicus' theory of the universe, and (were it possible) convince all men of its truth: but, since among the mass of students the idea is still unfamiliar, and the theory that the Earth is one of the Planets and moves among the Stars about the Sun, which is stationary, sounds to the most of them quite absurd, let those who are offended by the strangeness of this doctrine know that these harmonic speculations hold a place even among the hypotheses of Tycho Brahe. While that author agrees with Copernicus in regard to everything else which concerns the arrangement of the heavenly bodies and the laws governing their motions, the annual motion of the Earth alone, as held by Copernicus, he transfers to the whole system of the planetary orbits and to the Sun, which according to both authors is the centre of the system. For from this transference, motion results just the same, so that, if not in that utterly vast and immense space of the sphere of the fixed stars, at least in the system of the planetary world, the Earth holds at any one time the same place according to Brahe as is given to it by Copernicus. Furthermore, just as he who draws a circle on paper moves the writing foot of the compass around, while he who fastens the paper or a board to a revolving wheel keeps the foot of the compass or the style stationary and draws the same circle on the revolving board, so also on the present case; for Copernicus, the Earth measures out its orbit, between the outer circle of Mars and the inner circle of Venus, by the real motion of its own body, while for Tycho Brahe the whole planetary system (in which among the other orbits are also those of Mars and Venus) turns around like the board on the wheel, and brings to the stationary Earth, as to the style of the turner, the space between the orbits of Mars and Venus; and from this motion of the system it results that the Earth, itself remaining stationary, marks on Space the same course around the Sun, between Mars and Venus, which, according to Copernicus, it marks by the real motion of its own body with the system at rest. Since, then, the harmonic speculation considers the eccentric motions of the planets, as seen from the Sun, one can easily understand that, if an observer were on the Sun, however great the Sun's motion, the Earth, although it were at rest (to grant this for the moment to Brahe), would, nevertheless, seem to him to run its annual course in the space between the planets, and also in a time between the planet's times. Although, therefore, a man may be weak in faith and so unable to conceive of the motion of the Earth among the stars, he may still find it possible to take pleasure in the exalted contemplation of this most divine mechanism: he needs but to apply whatever he hears about the daily motions of the Earth in its eccentric to the appearance of those motions on the Sun, as even Tycho Brahe presents it with the Earth at rest.

The true followers of the Samian philosophy, however, have no just cause for envying such men this participation in a most delightful speculation, for if they accept also the immovability of the Sun and the motion of the Earth, their pleasure will be more exquisite in many ways, since it will be derived from the very consummated perfection of contemplation.

From *A Source Book in Astronomy* (**10**).

GALILEO THE POLEMICIST

In The Assayer, *published in 1623, Galileo replied with great power to an attack made by the Jesuit Father Grassi under the pseudonym of Sarsi. In the first of these passages Galileo ridicules the use of argument by analogy, although one should not take his apparent dismissal of the principle of circularity too seriously. In the second he makes his attitude towards the citation of 'authorities' quite explicit.*

Before I proceed let me tell Sarsi that it is not I who want the sky to have the noblest shape because of its being the noblest body; it is Aristotle himself, against whose views Sig. Guiducci is arguing. For my own part, never having read the pedigrees and patents of nobility of shapes, I do not know which of them are more and which are less noble, nor do I know their rank in perfection. I believe that in a way all shapes are ancient and noble; or, to put it better, that none of them are noble and perfect, or ignoble and imperfect, except in so far as for building walls a square shape is more perfect than the circular, and for wagon wheels the circle is more perfect then the triangle.

Sarsi says that abundant arguments have been supplied by me for proving the roughness of the interior surface of the sky, since I will have it that the moon and other planets—bodies which are also celestial, and even more noble and perfect than the sky itself—are mountainous and rough. And if that is so, he asks, why shouldn't irregularity exist also in the shape of the sky? For an answer to this let him put down whatever it is that he would reply to a man who argued that the surface of the ocean should be bony and scaly, since the fish which inhabit it are.

As to his question why the moon is not smooth, I reply that it and all the other planets are inherently dark and shine by light from the sun. Hence they must have rough surfaces, for if they were smooth as mirrors no reflection would reach us from them and they would be quite invisible to us. . . . On the other hand almost equal disorder would ensue if the celestial orbs were of a solid substance and had surfaces not perfectly smooth, since then refractions would be disturbed and the movements, shapes and projections of rays from the planets would be most confused and irregular.

Now let us go on to examine the arrows in flight and the lead balls hurled by catapults which are supposed to be set afire and melted in the air, according to the authority of Aristotle, many famous poets, other philosophers, and historians. But it is wrong to say, as Sarsi does, that Guiducci and I would laugh and joke at the experiences adduced by Aristotle. We merely do not believe that a cold arrow shot from a bow can take fire in the air; rather, we think that if an arrow were shot when afire, it would cool down more quickly than it would if it were held still. This is not derision; it is simply the statement of our opinion.

Sarsi goes on to say that since this experience of Aristotle's has failed to convince us, many other great men also have written things of the same sort. To this I reply that if in order to refute Aristotle's statement we are obliged to represent that no other men have believed it, then nobody on earth can ever refute it, since nothing can make those who have believed it not believe it. But is is news to me that any man would actually put the testimony of writers ahead of what experience shows him. To adduce more witnesses serves no purpose, Sarsi, for we have never denied that such things have been written and believed. We did say they are false, but so far as authority is concerned yours alone is as effective as an army's in rendering the events true or false. You take your stand on the authority of many poets against our experiments. I reply that if those poets could be present at our experiments they would change their views, and without disgrace they could say they had been writing hyperbolically—or even admit they had been wrong.

From *Discoveries and Opinions of Galileo* (5).

GALILEO: ABSTRACTIONISM IN PHYSICS

In this passage from his Dialogues concerning two New Sciences *Galileo makes his spokesman Sagredo reply to the objections of the Aristotelian Simplicio. Sagredo explains that the motions which we can actually observe are not the same as those on which physical calculations must be based.*

SAGR. One cannot deny that the argument is new, subtle and conclusive, resting as it does upon this hypothesis, namely, that the horizontal motion remains uniform, that the vertical motion continues to be accelerated downwards in proportion to the square of the time, and that such motions and velocities as these combine without altering, disturbing, or hindering each other, so that as the motion proceeds the path of the projectile does not change into a different curve: but this, in my opinion, is impossible. For the axis of the parabola along which we imagine the natural motion of a falling body to take place stands perpendicular to a horizontal surface, and ends at the centre of the earth; and since the parabola deviates more and more from its axis no projectile can ever reach the centre of the earth or, if it does, as seems necessary, then the path of the projectile must transform itself into some other curve very different from the parabola.

SIMPL. To these difficulties, I may add others. One of these is that we suppose the horizontal plane, which slopes neither up nor down, to be represented by a straight line as if each point on this line were equally distant from the centre, which is not the case; for one starts from the middle (of the line) and goes toward either end, he departs farther and farther from the centre (of the earth) and is therefore constantly going uphill. Whence it follows that the motion cannot remain uniform through any distance whatever, but must continually diminish. Besides, I do not see how it is possible to avoid the resistance of the medium which must destroy the uniformity of the horizontal motion and change the law of acceleration of falling bodies. These various changes render it highly improbable that a result derived from such reliable hypotheses should hold true in practice.

SALV. All these difficulties and objections which you urge are so well founded that it is impossible to remove them; and, as for me, I am ready to admit them all, which indeed I think our Author would also do. I grant that these conclusions proved in the abstract will be different when applied in the concrete and will be fallacious to this extent, that neither will the horizontal motion be uniform nor the natural acceleration be in the ratio assumed, nor the path of the projectile a parabola, etc. But, on the other hand, I ask you not to begrudge our Author that which other eminent men have assumed even if not strictly true. The authority of Archimedes alone will satisfy everybody. In his Mechanics and in his first quadrature of the parabola he takes for granted that the beam of a balance or steelyard is a straight line, every point of which is equidistant from the common centre of all heavy bodies, and that the cords by which heavy bodies are suspended are parallel to each other.

Some consider this assumption permissible because, in practice, our instruments and the distances involved are so small in comparison with the enormous distance from the centre of the earth that we may consider a minute of arc on a great circle as a straight line, and may regard the perpendiculars let fall from its two extremities as parallel. For if in actual practice one had to consider such small quantities, it would be necessary first of all to criticise the architects who presume, by use of a plumbline, to erect high towers with parallel sides. I may add that, in all their discussion, Archimedes and the others considered themselves as located at an infinite distance from the centre of the Earth, in which case their assumptions were not false, and therefore their conclusions were absolutely correct. When we wish to apply our proven conclusions to distances which, though finite, are very large, it is necessary for us to infer, on the basis of demonstrated truth, what correction is to be made for the fact that our distance from the centre of the earth is not really infinite, but merely very great in comparison with the small dimensions of our apparatus. The largest of these will be the range of our projectiles—and even here we need consider only the artillery—which, however great, will never exceed four of those miles of which as many thousand separate us from the centre of the earth; and since these paths terminate upon the surface of the earth only very slight changes can take place in their parabolic figure which, it is conceded, would be greatly altered if they terminated at the centre of the earth.

As to the perturbation arising from the resistance of the medium this is more considerable and does not, on account of its manifold forms, submit to fixed laws and exact description. Thus if we consider only the resistance which the air offers to the motions studied by us, we shall see that it disturbs them all and disturbs them in an infinite variety of ways corresponding to the infinite variety in the form, weight, and velocity of the projectiles.

From *Dialogues concerning Two New Sciences* (4).

document 7

DESCARTES: THE PHILOSOPHER AS SCIENTIST

These passages from the Principles of Philosophy *are typical of their author in their mixture of brilliant analysis with unjustifiable assertion and hypothesis. In the first Descartes discusses the creation of the world, in the second the mechanical operation of sense organs.*

Part III, 46
From what has already been said it is established that all bodies in the Universe consist of one and the same matter; that this is divisible arbitrarily into parts, and is actually divided into many pieces with various motions; that this motion is in a way circular, and that the same quantity of motion is constantly preserved on the Universe. We cannot determine by reason how big these pieces of matter are, how quickly they move, or what circles they describe. God might have arranged these things in countless different ways; which way he in fact chose rather than the rest is a thing we must learn from observation. Therefore, we are free to make any assumption we like about them, so long as all the consequences agree with experience. So by your leave, I shall suppose that all the matter constituting the visible world was originally divided by God into unsurpassably equal particles of medium size—that is of the average size of those that now form the heavens and the stars; that they had collectively just

the quantity of motion now found in the world; that . . . each turned round its own centre, so that they formed a fluid body, such as we take the heavens to be; and that many revolved together around various other points . . . and thus constituted as many different vortices as there now are stars in the world.

Part IV, 198

Moreover, we observe no difference between nerves to justify the view that something different is transmitted along different nerves from the external sense-organs to the brain; or that anything is transmitted to the brain at all, except the local motion of the nerves themselves. And we observe that this local motion can produce not only sensations of pain and enjoyment, but also those of light and sound. If somebody is struck in the eye, so that the vibration of the blow reaches the retina, he will see, just from this, a large number of dazzling sparks; and this light will have no existence outside the eye. Again, if someone stops his ear with his finger, he will hear a trembling murmur, arising merely from the motion of the air contained in the ear.

Finally, we often observe that heat and other sensible qualities in so far as they are objective, and even the [substantial] forms of purely material objects, e.g. the forms of fire, arise from the local motions of certain bodies, and themselves produce other local motion in other bodies. Now we understand very well how the varying size, shape, and motion of the particles of one body arouse various local motion in another body; but we can by no means understand how these proportions (size, shape, and motion) should produce something else of wholly different nature, like the substantial forms and real qualities that many people suppose to exist in objects; nor yet how these qualities or forms could subsequently arouse local motions in other bodies. . . . We therefore must on all counts conclude that the objective external realities that we designate by the words *light, colour, odour, flavour, sound,* or by names of tactile qualities such as *heat* and *cold,* and even the so-called *substantial forms,* are not recognisably anything other than the powers that objects have to set our nerves in motion in various ways, according to their own varied disposition.

From *Philosophical Writings* (**8**).

SYDENHAM: THE PROGRESSIVE PHYSICIAN

Dr Thomas Sydenham was one of the most advanced doctors of his time, and generally avoided the extreme methods favoured by some of his colleagues. He wrote this letter to John Locke in 1668 when the latter, who was the physician to the Earl of Shaftesbury, consulted him about the treatment of his patient. Shaftesbury had been suffering from an abcess which was to require constant attention until his death in 1683. Although the prescription may sound curious, many of the herbs it contains probably have some medical value.

I conceave itt by no meanes saff for his Lordshipp to stopp up the abcess, triall once having bin made of the unsuccessfulness of doing it and the flux of matter as yett seeming too much in proportion to the canale, and I judge it better to keepe it open with a silver pipe than a wax candle, in regard that from the use of a candle the matter will have the less opportunity to issue out and consequently the passage choak up. But I think 'twere better that the pipe were shorter because by the present length thereof his Lordshippe is liable to dangerous accidents following any unequal motion of the body which in process of time may easily happen from riding in a coach, stouping or the like; nor doth it seem to be suspected that the matter will not worke itselfe out when the orifice shall be kept open. I conceive itt may somewhat contributt to the discharge of the matter if my Lord shall lie on his left side or as much as he can an in regard the imposthume is depending if he shall lie with his upper parts low. I hold itt very unsaff to use injections of any sort because the cavity being depending, the liquor how agreeable soever in other respects will by lodging it selfe in any little cavities begett new impostumations to which those injections administer matter and by this means the cavity still enlarged. I should thinke that a drying drinke constantlye kept to for ordinary drinke would be more conducible to the drying up of this flux of matter and sweetening the whole mass of bloud and humors than anything whatsoever: nor doe I conceave that my Lord's spare habitt of body may discourage from this course, but rather contrary when 'tis notoriouslye knowne that a drying diett though used with greater severity than 'twill be necessary to putt my Lord upon, hath after a while rendered bodies that before were very emaciated now plumpe and vigorouse. But what 2 draughts in a day can signifie, and those too of a liquor so compounded that the greater respect is had to the uncertyne and conjecturall virtue of sanitives and the lesser to the certyne and sensible qualitie of Driers I cannot imagine.

This therefore with submission to those that know more I should advise.

That nothing be don to the part saveing the use of a pipe that may be made somewhat shorter or to be lengthened with a wax candle and that it be dressed once a day if the matter be much, once in 2 days if little.

That of the stronger sort of liquor halfe a pint be taken hott every morning 1 hour before his Lordshipp riseth, and the same quantity at night as soon as he is in his bedd.

That the smaller liquor be constantly drunke at his meales and at other times cold.

That he purge or take a clyster every 5th or 6th day. Lett his Lordshipp's diet be in proportion to this way att least lett suppinges be avoided.

The stronge liquor
Take of lime, 1 pound; throw it into a gallon of boyling hott water. When this hath stood and is cold scum itt; throw off the cleare and add to itt of other water one gallon more. Of Sarsaparilla 4 ounces. Burdocke rootes 2 ozs. Of China, santalum citrinum, lignum lentissimum, sassaphras, liquirish, raisons of the sun stoned of each one oz. Off shavings of harts horne and Cardus seedes of each halfe an ounce. Leafes of agrimony, speedwell, sanicle and the tops of Snt Johnswort of each one handfull. Infuse these all night together in a diett pott over hott embers. The next morning boyle them to the consuming of a third part. Then strayne it through a woolen cloth, and put it by in a cold place, in earthen bottles. You may make halfe the quantity at a time.

The smaller liquor
Is to be made of the same quantity of ingredients but a double quantity of water and without lime.

Printed in *Dr Thomas Sydenham, 1624–1689*, by K. Dewhurst (Wellcome Hist. Med. Lib. 1966).

THE NEWTONIAN SYNTHESIS

In this first extract from the Principia *Newton gives an exceptionally lucid account of the Galilean theory of projectile motion.*

Hitherto I have laid down such principles as have been received by mathematicians, and are confirmed by abundance of experiments. By the first two Laws and the first two Corollaries, *Galileo* discovered that the descent of bodies varied as the square of the time (*in duplicata ratione temporis*) and that the motion of projectiles was in the curve of a parabola; experience agreeing with both, unless so far as these motions are a little retarded by the resistance of the air. When a body is falling, the uniform force of its gravity acting equally, impresses, in equal intervals of time, equal forces upon that body, and therefore generates equal velocities; and in the whole time impresses a whole force, and generates a whole velocity proportional to the time. And the spaces described in proportional times are as the product of the velocities and the times; that is, as the squares of the times.

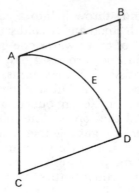

And when a body is thrown upwards, its uniform gravity impresses forces and reduces velocities proportional to the times; and the times of ascending to the greatest heights are as the velocities to be taken away, and those heights are as the product of the velocities and the times, or as the squares of the velocities. And if a body be projected in any direction, the motion arising from its projection is compounded with the motion arising from its gravity. Thus, if the body A by its motion of projection alone could describe in a given time the right line AB, and with its motion of falling alone could describe in the same time the altitude AC; complete the parallelogram ABCD, and the body by that compounded motion will at the end of the time be found in the place D; and the curved line AED, which that body describes, will be a parabola, to which the right line AB will be a tangent at A; and whose ordinate DB will be as the square of the line AB.

From *The Mathematical Principles of Natural Philosophy* (**6**): Scholium to the Axioms, or Laws of Motion.

In the second passage there are more technicalities; it is included both as an example of Newton's methods of argument and on account of its central importance.

The planets move in ellipses which have their common focus in the centre of the Sun; and, by radii drawn to that centre, they describe areas proportional to the times of description.

We have discoursed above on these motions from the Phenomena. Now that we know the principles on which they depend, from those principles we deduce the motion of the heavens *a priori*. Because the weights of the planets towards the sun are inversely as the squares of their distances from the sun's centre, if the sun were at rest, and the other planets did not act one upon another, their orbits would be ellipses, having the sun in their common focus; and they would describe areas proportional to the times of description, by Prop. I and XI, and Cor. I, Prop. XIII, Book I. But the actions of the planets one upon another are so very small, that they may be neglected; and by Prop. LXVI, Book I, they disturb the motions of the planets around the sun in motion, less than if those motions were performed about the sun at rest.

It is true that the action of Jupiter upon Saturn is not to be neglected; for the force of gravity towards Jupiter is to the force of gravity towards the sun (at equal distances, (Cor. II, Prop. VIII) as 1 to 1067; and therefore in the conjunction of Jupiter and Saturn, because the distance of Saturn from Jupiter is to the distance of Saturn from the Sun almost as 4 to 9, the gravity of Saturn towards Jupiter will be to the gravity of Saturn towards the sun as 81 to 16·1067; or, as 1 to about 211. And hence arises a perturbation of the orbit of Saturn in every conjunction of this planet with Jupiter, so sensible, that astronomers are puzzled with it. As the planet is differently situated in these conjunctions, its eccentricity is sometimes augmented, sometimes diminished; its aphelion is sometimes carried forwards, sometimes backwards, and its mean motion is by turns accelerated and retarded; yet the whole error in its motion about the sun, though arising from so great a force, may be almost avoided (except in the mean motion) by placing the lower focus of its orbit in the common centre of gravity of Jupiter and the sun (according to Prop. LXVII, Book I), and therefore that error, when it is greatest, scarcely exceeds two minutes; and the greatest error in the mean motion scarcely exceeds two minutes yearly. But in the conjunction of Jupiter and Saturn, the accelerative forces of gravity of the sun towards Saturn, of Jupiter towards Saturn, and of Jupiter towards the sun, are almost as

$$16,\ 81,\ \text{and}\ \frac{16.81.3021}{25}\ ,\ \text{or}\ 156609;$$

and therefore the difference of the forces of gravity of the sun towards Saturn, and of Jupiter towards Saturn, is to the force of gravity of Jupiter towards the sun as 65 to 156609, or as 1 to 2409. But the greatest power of Saturn to disturb the motion of Jupiter is proportional to this difference, and therefore the perturbation of the orbit of Jupiter is much less than that of Saturn's. The perturbations of the other orbits are yet far less, except that the orbit of the earth is sensibly disturbed by the moon. The common centre of gravity of the earth and moon moves in an ellipse about the sun in the focus thereof, and, by a radius drawn to the sun, describes areas proportional to the times of description. But the earth in the meantime by a menstrual motion is revolved about this common centre.

Mathematical Principles . . . , Book III, Proposition XIII, Theorem XIII.

The final passage contains a famous general description of the Newtonian world, with particular emphasis on atoms and gravitation.

112

**The qualities of bodies, which admit neither intensi-
fication nor remission of degrees, and which are found
to belong to all bodies within the reach of our experiments, are to be esteemed the universal qualities of all
bodies whatsoever.**

For since the qualities of bodies are only known to us by experiments, we are to hold for universal all such as universally
agree with experiments; and such as are not liable to diminution
can never be quite taken away. We are certainly not to relin-
quish the evidence of experiments for the sake of dreams and
vain fictions of our own divising; nor are we to recede from the
analogy of Nature, which is wont to be simple, and always
consonant to itself. We in no other way know the extension of
bodies than by our senses, nor do these reach it in all bodies;
but because we perceive extension in all that are sensible, therefore we ascribe it universally to all others also. That abundance
of bodies are hard, we learn by experience; and because the
hardness of the whole arises from the hardness of the parts, we
therefore justly infer the hardness of the undivided particles not
only of the bodies we feel but of all others. That all bodies are
impenetrable, we gather not from reason but from sensation.
The bodies which we handle we find impenetrable, and thence
conclude impenetrability to be an universal property of all
bodies whatsoever. That all bodies are movable, and endowed
with certain powers (which we call the inertia) of persevering
in their motion, or in their rest, we only infer from the like
properties observed in the bodies which we have seen. The extension, hardness, impenetrability, mobility, and inertia of the
whole, result from the extension, hardness, impenetrability,
mobility, and inertia of the parts; and hence we conclude the
least particles of all bodies to be also all extended, and hard and
impenetrable, and movable, and endowed with their proper
inertia. And this is the foundation of all philosophy. Moreover,
that the divided but contiguous particles of bodies may be
separated from one another, is matter of observation; and in
the particles that remain undivided, our minds are able to dis-
tinguish yet lesser parts, as is mathematically demonstrated.
But whether the parts so distinguished, and not yet divided,
may, by the powers of Nature, be actually divided and separated

from one another, we cannot certainly determine. Yet, had we the proof of but one experiment that any undivided particle, in breaking a hard and solid body, suffered a division, we might by virtue of this rule conclude that the undivided as well as the divided particles may be divided, and actually separated to infinity.

Lastly, if it universally appears, by experiments and astronomical observations, that all bodies about the earth gravitate towards the earth, and that in proportion to the quantity of matter which they severally contain; that the moon likewise, according to the quantity of its matter, gravitates towards the earth; that, on the other hand, our sea gravitates towards the moon; and all the planets one towards another; and the comets in like manner towards the sun; we must, in consequence of this rule, universally allow that all bodies whatsoever are endowed with a principle of mutual gravitation. For the argument from the appearances concludes with more force for the universal gravitation of all bodies than for their impenetrability; of which, among those in the celestial regions, we have no experiments, nor any manner of observation. Not that I affirm gravity to be essential to bodies: by their *vis insita* I mean nothing but their inertia. This is immutable. Their gravity is diminished as they recede from the earth.

Mathematical Principles . . . , Book III, Rule III.

Bibliography

PRIMARY SOURCES

For the history of science the published works of notable scientists are generally more important than other documents. But they are not always easy of access, particularly for those who cannot read Latin or French. The scientific works of Copernicus, Kepler and Descartes, to mention only the most obvious examples, are difficult or impossible to obtain in adequate English translations. The following list is therefore partial in its coverage.

1 Bacon, Francis, *The Works*, ed. J. Spedding, R. L. Ellis and D. D. Heath, London 1857.

2 Boyle, Robert, *Works*, ed. T. Birch, London 1744.

3 Galileo, *Dialogue concerning the Two Chief World Systems—Ptolemaic and Copernican*, trans. S. Drake, Univ. of California Press 1953.

4 Galileo, *Dialogues concerning Two New Sciences*, trans. H. Crew and A. de Salvio, Constable 1962. Despite its title this is a translation of the *Discorsi*.

5 Galileo, *Discoveries and Opinions of Galileo*, trans. S. Drake, Doubleday Anchor 1957.

6 Newton, Isaac, *Mathematical Principles of Natural Philosophy*, Andrew Motte's 1729 translation revised by F. Cajori, Univ. of California Press 1934.

7 Newton, Isaac, *Opticks*, Bell 1931.

8 Descartes, René, *Philosophical Writings*, sel. and trans. E. Anscombe and P. T. Geach, Nelson 1954.

9 Sprat, Thomas, *History of the Royal Society*, ed. by Cope and Jones, Routledge 1959.

10 Shapley, H. and Howarth, H. E., ed., *A Source Book in Astronomy* Harvard U.P. 1929.

11 Leicester, H. M. and Klickstein, H. S., ed., *A Source Book in Chemistry*, Harvard U. P. 1952.

12 Magie, W. F., ed., *A Source Book in Physics*, Harvard U.P. 1935.

13 Kearney, H. F., *Origins of the Scientific Revolution*, Longmans 1964.

GENERAL STUDIES

14 Neugebauer, O., *The Exact Sciences in Antiquity*, Harper Torchbooks 1962.

15 Sambursky, S., *The Physical World of the Greeks*, Routledge 1956.

16 Farrington, B., *Greek Science*, Penguin Books 1955.

17 Clagett, M., *Greek Science in Antiquity*, Collier 1963.

18 Clagett, M., ed., *The Science of Mechanics in the Middle Ages*, Univ. of Wisconsin Press 1959.

19 Crombie, A. C., *Augustine to Galileo*, Heinemann 1961.

20 Dijksterhuis, E. J., *The Mechanisation of the World Picture*, Oxford U.P. 1961.

21 Singer, C. *et al*, eds. *A History of Technology*, Oxford U.P. 1954-8.

22 Taton, R., ed., *A General History of the Sciences*, Thames and Hudson, 1963. 2 vols.

23 Boas, M., *The Scientific Renaissance, 1450-1630*, Collins 1962.

24 Butterfield, H., *The Origins of Modern Science, 1300-1800*, Bell 1957.

25 Hall, A. R., *The Scientific Revolution*, Longmans 1954.

26 Hall, A. R., *From Galileo to Newton, 1630-1720*, Collins 1963.

27 Burtt, E. A., *The Metaphysical Foundations of Modern Science*, Routledge 1932.

28 Wightman, W. P. D., *Science and the Renaissance*, Oliver & Boyd 1962.

29 Clagett, M., ed., *Critical Problems in the History of Science*, Univ. of Wisconsin Press 1959.

30 Koyré, A., *From the Closed World to the Infinite Universe*, Harper Torchbooks 1958.

31 Gillespie, G. C., *The Edge of Objectivity*, Princeton U.P. 1960.

BOOKS ON SPECIFIC TOPICS

Astronomy

32 Kuhn, T. S., *The Copernican Revolution*, Harvard U.P. 1957.

33 Johnson, F. R., *Astronomical Thought in Renaissance England*, Johns Hopkins Press 1937.

34 Koestler, A., *The Sleepwalkers*, Hutchinson 1959.

35 Taylor, E. G. R., *The Haven-Finding Art*, Hollis & Carter 1956.

Chemistry

36 Holmyard, E. J., *Alchemy*, Penguin Books 1957.

116

37 Boas, M., *Robert Boyle and Seventeenth-Century Chemistry*, Cambridge U.P. 1958.

Medicine

38 Cole, F. J., *A History of Comparative Anatomy*, Macmillan 1944.
39 Clark, G. N., *The History of the Royal College of Physicians of London*, Oxford U.P. 1964.
40 Pagel, W., *Paracelsus*, Karger 1958.
41 Debus, A. G., *The English Paracelsians*, Oldbourne 1965.
42 O'Malley, C. D., *Andreas Vesalius of Brussels*, Univ. of California Press 1964.
43 Keynes, G., *William Harvey*, Oxford U.P. 1965.

Physics

44 Dugas, R., *Mechanics in the Seventeenth Century*, Griffon 1958.
45 Geymonat, L., *Galileo Galilei*, McGraw-Hill 1965.
46 Koyré, *Metaphysics and Measurement*, Chapman & Hall 1968.
47 Koyré, A., *Newtonian Studies*, Chapman & Hall 1965.
48 More, L. T., *Isaac Newton*, Scribner 1934.
49 Harré, R., *Matter and Method*, Macmillan 1964.

Organisations

50 Curtis, M. H., *Oxford and Cambridge in Transition, 1558–1642*, Oxford U.P. 1959.
51 Brown, H., *Scientific Organisations in Seventeenth Century France*, Russell and Russell 1967.
52 Hartley, H., ed., *The Royal Society; Its Origins and Founders*, Royal Society 1960.
53 Purver, M., *The Royal Society; Concept and Creation*, Routledge 1967. (A highly contentious and, in my view, very misleading study.)

General Intellectual History and Various

54 Lovejoy, A. O., *The Great Chain of Being*, Harvard U.P. 1936.
55 Tillyard, E. M. W., *The Elizabethan World Picture*, Chatto 1943; Penguin Books 1963.
56 Willey, B., *The Seventeenth Century Background*, Chatto 1934; Penguin Books 1962.
57 Jones, R. F., *Ancients and Moderns*, Washington U.P. 1936.
58 Hill, J. E. C., *Intellectual Origins of the English Revolution*, Oxford U.P. 1965.

117

59 Rhys, H. H., ed., *Seventeenth Century Science and the Arts*, Princeton U.P. 1963.

60 Walker, D. P., *Spiritual and Demonic Magic from Ficino to Campanella*, Warburg Institute 1959.

61 Yates, F. A., *Giordano Bruno and the Hermetic Tradition*, Routledge 1964.

62 Yates, F. A., *The Art of Memory*, Routledge 1966.

63 Rossi, P., *Francis Bacon; From Magic to Science*, Routledge 1968.

64 'Espinasse, M., *Robert Hooke*, Heinemann 1956.

65 Clark, G. N., *Science and Social Welfare in the Age of Newton*, Oxford U.P. 1937.

66 Taylor, E. G. R., *The Mathematical Practitioners of Tudor and Stuart England*, Cambridge U.P. 1954.

ARTICLES

No attempt will be made here to give a list of even the most important articles available in learned journals. No serious student can afford to neglect periodicals such as *The Journal of the History of Ideas, Isis, Osiris, Ambix, History of Science, Annals of Science* etc. But these are only available in specialist libraries, and are covered in fuller bibliographies. The journal *Past and Present* should be much more readily accessible, and the following articles are of special interest:

67 Mason, S. F., Science and religion in seventeenth-century England (3).

68 'Espinasse, M., The decline and fall of Restoration science (14).

69 Kearney, H. F., Puritanism, capitalism, and the scientific revolution (28).

70 Hill, C., Puritanism, capitalism, and the scientific revolution (29).

71 Kearney, H. F., Puritanism and science; problems of definition (31).

72 Rabb, T. K., Religion and the rise of modern science (31).

73 Hill, C., Science, religion and society in the 16th and 17th centuries (32).

74 Rabb, T. K., Science, religion and society in the 16th and 17th centuries (33).

75 Shapiro, B. J., Latitudinarianism and science (40).

Index

119